Healthy Body, Peaceful Earth, Loving Heart

The Compassionate Jewel of Vegan Buddhism

The Buddha, The Vegan, and You:

Part 2

John Bussineau

GW00642981

Calm Water Publishing

West Bloomfield, 2017

Notice

All material in this book is provided for your information
only and may not be construed as medical advice or
instruction. Readers should consult appropriate health
professionals on any matter relating to their health and
well-being. The information given here and the sharing of
my personal experiences are designed to help you make
more informed decisions about your health. It is not
intended as a substitute for any treatment that may have
been prescribed by your doctor. If you suspect that you
have a medical problem, you are urged you to seek
competent medical help. Mention of specific companies,
organizations, or authorities in this book does not imply
endorsement by the author or publisher, nor does
mention of specific companies, organizations, or
authorities imply they endorse this book.

Table of Contents

Forward

Causes and Conditions

Summer retreat 1997 was my entry into the world of
Tibetan Buddhism. I had been going to weekly lectures
and teachings since January of that year but resolved to
immerse myself in a 10-day retreat. A socially awkward
introvert, I drove alone to the Lake Copneconic YMCA
complex 30 miles north of Detroit to register. I was
nervous not knowing what I had gotten myself into. I
found registration, picked up my materials, acquired my
bunk assignment and headed off to help set up. This was
the last week of summer in Michigan and the camp was
devoid of any children, who were now home prepping for
the new school year. The expectation of autumn was in
the air, as was my anticipation to study The Lam Rim—
something new, challenging, and profound. Coming early
as a volunteer I found myself in what was to be the main
teaching area, where 225 people would be sitting on
cushions listening to teachings and meditating. About ten
people were erecting a large stage with an altar and
backdrop for numerous large colorful thangkas (Tibetan
paintings) to hang on each end. The center of the altar
contained a 3-foot golden Buddha. A teaching seat for the
guru was 10 feet in front of the Buddha statue and was
much lower.

It was here I first met Dan and Bill. They were
both extremely friendly and took me under their wing,
explaining the grounds, process of the retreat, and
logistics. Both were successful businessmen with a
penchant for meditation, compassion, and a burning
desire for the acquisition of wisdom. Bill was quite
adamant and convincing about what Buddhism stood for

to him, "It is all logic, John, every bit of it. Sure, there are people who focus on only the mystical end of things, but they are nuts. Buddhism's true essence is all based on logic and analysis. If it doesn't add up, if it doesn't come through the crucible fire of pure, lucid reasoning—it's all bullshit."

This resonated with me and I vividly remember it today, 20 years later. It has always been a central and foundational brick upon which I could build an allegiance with this ancient, mysterious, and foreign thought process. Buddhism aligned with my love of science and the scientific method of discovery: observation, theory, experimentation and testing, and review to see if results actually fit the theoretic model.

I was a nerdy kid growing up. My father committed suicide when I was age 4 and I lost myself in study: reading books; playing with chemistry sets and microscopes; and learning biology, geology, ham radio, and science in all functions. Science fiction, the U.S. space program, and especially astronomy were passions. At age 11 I was never more excited than when my 6-inch mirror kit arrived from Edmund Scientific, so I could begin grinding it into a parabola and build my own reflector telescope. During Siberia-like sub-zero Michigan winter nights, you could find me alone in the backyard, exploring the skies. As any astronomer knows, the colder the night, the clearer the sky—and the first time I split the rings of Saturn with my telescope was pure euphoria.

That was looking out. And Buddhism, while similar, has an opposite characteristic, as it looks inward while using some of the same tools: observation, analysis, concentration, meditation, insight, and then implementation in one's life.

Tenzin Gyatso, His Holiness the 14th Dalai Lama, states,

> "In one sense the methods of science and Buddhism are different: Scientific investigation proceeds by experiment, using instruments that analyze external phenomena, whereas contemplative investigation proceeds by the development of refined attention, which is then used in the introspective examination of inner experience. But both share a strong empirical basis: If science shows something to exist or to be nonexistent, then we must acknowledge that as a fact. If a hypothesis is tested and found to be true, we must accept it. Likewise, Buddhism must accept the facts—whether found by science or by contemplative insights. If, when we investigate something, we find there is reason and proof for it, we must acknowledge that as reality—even if it is in contradiction with a literal scriptural explanation that has held sway for many centuries or with a deeply held opinion or view. So, one fundamental attitude shared by Buddhism and science is the commitment to keep searching for reality by empirical means and to be willing to disregard accepted or long-held positions if our search finds the truth is different."[1]

This was a lesson I learned at the first retreat, too: Test it, analyze it, and when you know it to be pure, then buy into it. The analogy the Buddha was said to have taught was around the purchasing of gold. One should not buy gold just because a seller said it was pure. Not until the purchaser had tested it against all the properties of gold known at that time—its softness, its melting point, its ability to never tarnish. Just so, all things in life are to be treated as testing for gold, including the spiritual path. Nothing is to be taken purely on someone else's word. Blind faith is not what the Buddha taught, but rather intelligent faith based on a method of inquiry, testing, and analysis.

The Buddha cared about his health and the health of his followers, sangha, and community. He cared about people and animals. Health was not something to be attached to but also not to be discarded, as he found while doing ascetic practice for 6 years prior to this enlightenment and almost starved himself to death. He cared for life and the planet. Central to all Buddhist teachings is a reverence for the web of life, our mutual dependence on one another. This principle relates to the doctrine of dependent origination, the concepts of emptiness or voidness, and the King of Logic, where all phenomena happen due to causes and conditions. Emptiness or voidness is not nothingness but rather the opposite, and the knowledge that all things lack an inherent existence (independently on their own). Phenomena, it is taught, are inextricably connected in a web of unbreakable relativity based on their conditions and causes. The Buddha taught:

- When this is, that is.
- From the arising of this, comes the arising of that.
- When this isn't, that isn't.
- From the cessation of this, comes the cessation of that.

Conditions change, Buddhism informs us, as all created phenomena are impermanent. When conditions change, a new analysis may be needed, based on the new situations and empirical evidence. For instance, are the deeply held opinions and habits related to eating meat, fish, dairy, and eggs holistic, healthy, and ethical in 2017? What does the science say about health today? Are we informed by science that the eating of meat, fish, dairy and eggs is a healthy habit or an unhealthy one? Where is the data and evidence, and what does it suggest? What about the environment? Is there a connection between what 7 billion humans choose to eat and the environmental crisis we find ourselves in today?

Most importantly, if as a Buddhist practitioner or any spiritual person who lives a logical life based on reason and compassion, what should we do when we find we are harming our health, sickening and perhaps even killing ourselves early? What is the ethical thing to do? Should we investigate the changing causes and conditions, which are the foundation of any transformation for moral and ethical behavior? The Buddha taught that when situations change we should use wisdom to analyze them and make changes accordingly.

This is called situational ethics[2], whereby each society and person must decide for themselves the ethical implication of their actions. How should our society deal with the current situation of health and environmental crises? Do the causes and conditions we are confronted with today inform us to change? I believe yes. Please consider the following:

- The eating of animal products unequivocally has been shown to cause disease states through medical and scientific investigations. Through hard, verifiable, peer-reviewed data, we know eating cows, pigs, chickens, fish, dairy, and eggs create the situational conditions and causes for illnesses, such as but not limited to heart disease, cancers, and diabetes.

- The data shows that the production of beef, pork, chicken, dairy, fish, and eggs is a major cause for pollution, global warming, and depletion of our planet's resources. They contribute heavily to greenhouse gases, dead zones, desertification, rain forest destruction, melting polar caps, fresh water shortages, and food scarcity. Eating animals is the single largest factor in global depletion of all resources, and even if we eliminated all fossil fuel usage by industry and transportation today, this very minute, we would still exceed our COP greenhouse gas out-of-danger budget by 2050 (the amount of greenhouse gas we can burn and still keep global warming under 2 degrees Celsius).[3][4]
- We breed, enslave, and kill 70 billion land animals against their will annually. According to the Buddha—and now neuroscientists from the University of Cambridge 2,500 years later—we know they have sentience and consciousness.[5][6][7] We know they feel, have wants and needs, yet we keep them prisoners in hellish conditions and kill them against their will. This seems to run against the humane foundation for all human beings, let alone Buddhists, whose moral universe is *Sabbe Sattva* (Pali for "all beings").

When we analyze the situation today, we find no good reason for the unnecessary habit of eating meat, fish, dairy, and eggs. When we analyze the cause and conditions around eating meat, fish, dairy, and eggs we find only suffering in the form of poor health; disease; obesity; diabetes; cancer; global warming; fresh water scarcity; rainforest destruction; destruction of oceans, land, and habitat; and the sixth great extinction. We reap what we sow, and when we analyze the situation, any sane person would come to the conclusion that we should eliminate this habit and addiction. We know if we keep doing what we've always done, we will get the results we always have gotten. Shouldn't we intensely consider what is the most compassionate, loving, and wise course of action to take for our own selves, the planet, and the animals?

I will never forget a short conversation between two people I admire: Carl Sagan and His Holiness the Dalai Lama. Sagan asked the Dalai Lama if science could prove without a doubt that Buddhist doctrines, such as reincarnation, were inaccurate or did not exist, what would Buddhists do? The Dalai Lama replied that Buddhists would have to accept, "if through thorough investigation things become clear, only then is it time to accept and believe," he said.[8] [9] [10]

Whether one believes in reincarnation or not is immaterial; the point is that Buddhists and all people of reason should consider making changes in their lives when evidence establishes that something which was formerly believed and acted upon causes negativity and harm. The inner science of Buddhism teaches us to analyze our emotions, thoughts, and behaviors to find out where these things cause us to harm ourselves or others. We find through the introspective tools which Buddhism and other meditative techniques provide that thoughts, emotions, and behaviors in many cases are suppressed and we may be in a state of denial. Long-held views and opinions have this quality. Where we find we have been suppressing something, it should be brought to light, tested, analyzed—and changed when it is a cause for us to create negativity. People of intention should strongly consider discarding habits which cause suffering of themselves and others, because we can change our minds and behavior.

One core Buddhist teaching is that this life is precious due to our abilities to change ourselves in any way we choose; our minds have magnificent elasticity. Also, traditional Buddhist teachings state that getting a human rebirth is a rarity. If this life is precious and rare, shouldn't we make the most of it and change the habits causing disease and destruction to ourselves and our environment?

The evidence is here. We know what we are doing to our own precious human health, the planet, and the animals, if we choose to look. This book contemplates some of the overwhelming data that solidly supports a needed change to opinions and behaviors long antiquated and invalidated.

The Body

But those who always practice well bodily mindfulness, do never what should not be done and ever do what should be done; mindful, clearly comprehending, their pollutions out of existence go.

Well awake and watchful ever are Gotama's savaka, who constantly by day and night are mindful of the body.

Dhammapada, Verses 293 and 299[11]

This Precious Human Form

After the Buddha gained enlightenment under the Bodhi tree, he went through a period of wonderment at what he had found. He didn't know how he was going to be able to communicate the enlightened state. He came to grips with it after a few weeks and traveled to Benares, now known as Varanasi, to a place called Deer Park. It was here he met up with his former colleagues, with whom he had spent years searching for liberation and an end to suffering. It was here he gave the first teaching. This teaching was on the Four Noble Truths: the truth of suffering, the cause of suffering, the fact we can escape suffering, and the path enabling us to do so. Part of this teaching was letting his former companions know that starving, mutilating, and depriving one's body would not help with becoming enlightened. He had learned this when he had come close to death in Sujata's village, and thus he began teaching about the Middle Path, where one does not deprive one's body. We should care for our bodies, keep our bodies strong and healthy because there is a body-mind connection, and if we are to be successful in our meditation practices we should have a sound physical body. He told his former colleagues, "To keep the body in good health is a duty, for otherwise we shall not be able to...keep our mind strong and clear." [12]

In the Lam Rim, the teachings brought by Atisha from India to Tibet, it is taught that this life is precious because a human rebirth has many endowments and capabilities. Humans hold a special place in the Buddhist cosmology, and putting arguments of speciesist attitudes aside, it is taught we have the capabilities to become enlightened, just as the Buddha, whereas animals or other beings (beings in hell realms, hungry ghosts, and god realms) do not. So it follows that we should be careful with our bodies and keep them healthy, since they are part of the "precious vehicle" to help us to awaken. As Je Tsongkhapa states in The Foundation of All Perfections, a short Lam Rim teaching,

> Precious human life, gained but once,
> Has great potential but is easily lost.
> Empower me to remember this constantly
> And to think day and night of taking its essence. [13]

This life is precious. We don't know how we got here. We don't know if we will gain a human rebirth again. We should take advantage of it, it is impermanent, and we can easily die. The teachings inform us we are no different from the Buddha. He had a human life. We have a human life. He achieved enlightenment, nirvana, and peace, and we can do the same. We have the same capacity and we should not squander this opportunity. So what is the Buddha telling us in his first teaching? Is he telling us to exercise? Is he telling us to eat organic food? Certainly exercise and food play the largest role in keeping our physical bodies healthy. Does this outlook advise us to ask ourselves, "What is the best way to keep our bodies healthy?" The answer is unequivocally, yes, but if we are to follow the Buddha's advice, what is the best food to eat?

The Curtain of Delusion: meat is good for you!

The myths we have told over and over begin to ring true. Here are but a few:

> "My parents and grandparents told me eating meat was good for me to be healthy."

> "I learned in school that eating meat, fish, dairy, and eggs was necessary to get the right amount of protein."

> "I was sick and my spiritual teacher told me to eat meat. He said we all need to eat some meat to be healthy."

> "Protein from animals is one of the food groups; it's healthy for you."

As a child of 12, I witnessed my loving Aunt Elda die of cancer. She had been an angel in my life, and next to the death of my father when I was 4 years old, Elda's death hurt me intensely. It impacted my outlook on impermanence and the truth of suffering early on.

I can remember my devoted Italian grandparents going to the store and buying a beef steak and/or beef liver, cooking it, and with love, compelling my aunt to eat these high-quality-protein foods. These foods, along with drinking whole milk, were urged even if she protested. I'll never forget the words of my grandmother, *La carne è un bene per il sangue.* (Meat is good for the blood.) And my aunt ate. She was diagnosed with ovarian cancer at about age 22 and died 10 years later. Watching her perish made us all feel powerless. There was nothing we could do and there was nothing we could say, except to be with her as she withered and died. She was getting the best medical care and eating the best food. She had the love of her family but had been doomed by this catastrophic disease. It had come out of nowhere and she just got it. If meat was good for the blood, what was wrong here? Why wasn't she getting better? Was it genetic? Did we all carry the genes for cancer? For my entire life, I and the rest of my family have been haunted with the specter of the genetic question: Are we next?

My grandparents were wrong. It turns out we don't need meat, fish, dairy, or eggs to be healthy. In fact, there is overwhelming evidence to the contrary, showing that the eating of animal products is associated with higher risk for many of the diseases we think are untreatable, genetic, and "just happen to us" (like the cancer many of our loved ones get). While we were trying to comfort my Aunt Elda and promote health we were actually promoting cancer by feeding her a diet high in animal protein.

It is now well known that diets low in animal protein inhibit cancer growth, as Dr. T. Colin Cambpell, PhD, writes in *The China Study:* "Dietary protein proved to be so powerful in its effect that we could turn on and off cancer growth simply by changing the level consumed ... We found that not all proteins had this effect. What protein consistently and strongly promoted cancer? Casein, which makes up 87% of cow's milk protein, and promoted all stages of the cancer process. What type of protein did not promote cancer, even at high levels of intake? The safe proteins were from plants, including wheat and soy. As this picture came into view, it began to challenge and then to shatter some of my most cherished assumptions."[14]

What scientific research is showing today is the opposite of what most of us have been taught. Eating a high-protein, animal-based diet promotes disease. Eating a pure vegan diet based on whole foods is the best diet for stimulating health and well-being. We do not need the protein in the flesh of animals, and quite the contrary to the common myth, animal protein is implicated in many disease states.

Have we been deluded by our families, culture, business, and society? Based on scientific evidence it would appear so. It would also appear as if the more compassionate, least harmful way to eat would also be the way to best feed our bodies. My grandparents feeding my aunt a high-animal-protein diet was actually helping the cancer rather than fighting it. Feeding her beef steak, liver, and milk every day promoted her disease. In fact, it appears that many disease states we exhibit are prevented, suspended, or cured by eating a whole-food, plant-based diet (WFPB).

It is worthwhile to consider the position on vegetarian and vegan diets by the American Dietetic Association:

> Appropriately planned vegetarian diets, including total vegetarian or vegan diets, are healthful, nutritionally adequate, and may provide health benefits in the prevention and treatment of certain diseases," the position paper authors write.

> "Well-planned vegetarian diets are appropriate for individuals during all stages of the life cycle, including pregnancy, lactation, infancy, childhood, and adolescence, and for athletes.... Food and nutrition professionals can assist vegetarian clients by providing current, accurate information about vegetarian nutrition, foods, and resources. [15]

Regardless of this and other affirmations, most of us continue to get a nagging feeling that we are going to miss something in our diet and take a health risk. We still believe, even though the evidence is overpoweringly contrary, that meat, fish, dairy, and eggs are needed in order to be healthy. Donald Hensrud, MD, from Mayo Clinic, turns this question around and asks,

> When people think of drastically reducing or even eliminating meat and other animal products from their diet, their first thought is often: 'What are the nutritional risks?' I suggest that this question be flipped around. It's really more valid to

ask: "What are the risks of continuing to eat meat?"[16]

In 2016, the Academy of Nutrition and Dietetics provided this position as published in the U.S. National Library of Medicine:

> Plant-based diets are more environmentally sustainable than diets rich in animal products because they use fewer natural resources and are associated with much less environmental damage. Vegetarians and vegans are at reduced risk of certain health conditions, including ischemic heart disease, type 2 diabetes, hypertension, certain types of cancer, and obesity. Low intake of saturated fat and high intakes of vegetables, fruits, whole grains, legumes, soy products, nuts, and seeds (all rich in fiber and phytochemicals) are characteristics of vegetarian and vegan diets that produce lower total and low-density lipoprotein cholesterol levels and better serum glucose control. These factors contribute to reduction of chronic disease.[17]

Unfortunately for my aunt, the risk and outcome was death at age 32. This was true for her and many millions of others today and is the reason why many medical doctors are advocating for their patients to eat a WFPB diet that is free of all animal products. While some believe one or two servings of meat per week are acceptable, the case for elimination of all animal products from one's diet to enable health and longer life is clear. Dr. Joel Fuhrman has been treating patients for many years using a WFPB diet with great success. Dr. Fuhrman advocates for a "nutrient-rich diet" made up of plant-based whole foods[18] and believes the diseases which afflict us and eventually kill us can for the most part be avoided. He has shown in his practice that patients can have a high-quality life, free of disease, remaining mentally and physically active into old age. The key is learning to live by eating with the nutritional quality found in a WFPB diet.[19]

But Isn't It All Genetics?

Kathy Freston states, "If you're anything like me, the 'C' word leaves you trembling. But today there is very good news to report: Research suggests you can improve your odds of never getting cancer and/or improve your chances of recovering from it. Not with a drug or surgery, although those methods might be quite effective. This is all about the power on your plate, and it's seriously powerful."[20]

The power that Kathy writes about is the power of diet to turn gene expression on or off and the power to lower other risk factors for cancer. So while you may have a gene that is a marker for cancer or some other disease, it appears that diet can trump the gene by turning it off.[21]

This means that we are not helpless, as I and so many others have thought our entire lives. The power to take control of our precious lives is truly in our own hands with the food choices we make. In a study from Loma Linda University and funded by the National Cancer Institute, Kathy Freston reports, "vegans have lower rates of cancer than both meat-eaters and vegetarians. Vegan women, for example, had 34% lower rates of female-specific cancers such as breast, cervical, and ovarian cancer. And this was compared to a group of healthy omnivores who ate substantially less meat than the general population (two servings a week or longer, as well as after controlling for non-dietary factors such as smoking, alcohol, and a family history of cancer."[22] These findings from the Loma Linda study correlate with findings from The China Study where it was discussed that animal protein promotes the growth of cancer and non-animal protein does not. Indeed, as researchers from *The China Study* found they could turn on and turn off cancer growth simply by raising and lowering levels of casein (the main protein in cow's milk).[23]

As one delves into this topic further, one learns there are various generalized stages in cancer cell growth. One is initiation and another is promotion. Our body may be genetically prone to initiate a certain cancer, given the right circumstances, but it seems we can affect its promotion (growth) by creating an environment it likes by eating animal products or an environment it dislikes by eating only whole foods in the form of plants. An extremely simplistic analogy would be the growth of a seed into a plant. We initiate the growth by putting the seed in the ground in a sunny location. Next we water the seed and provide nutrients (fertilizer). But if we stop watering, the seed will not grow. We may all have seeds for cancer, but do our bodies let them grow?

Work in this area is called epigenetics and has been pioneered Dr. Dean Ornish and Nobel Prize winner Elizabeth Blackburn[24]. Epigenetics basically shows us that genes of a disease must be turned on to operate, and we all have the ability through lifestyle changes to turn on good genes and turn off bad genes. It's up to us. Our genes, it turns out, are not our fate. This is extremely hopeful for not only various cancers but also heart disease. As Joel Kahn, MD, suggests, providing our body with the correct "raw material" will keep us healthy by "switching" on genes that promote heart health, lower cholesterol, keep our blood pressure at proper levels, and help our bodies regulate and keep other disease risk factors under control.[25] Indeed, Ornish and colleagues show in the Gene Expression Modulation by Intervention with Nutrition and Lifestyle (GEMINAL), that 500 genes showed a boosting of "disease-preventing genes" just from a short, 3-month change in diet for men with prostate cancer.[26] [27] [28]

When my aunt was struggling as a young woman to rid her body of cancer, I wish we had known about this. My family, as would most families, was doing what we thought best by feeding her the healthiest diet known. Protein, that magical substance which caused health and well-being, was what we all sought in large quantities and in high quality. But we didn't know much about protein, we only knew that it was in meat, fish, dairy, and eggs, and we needed to eat these foods every day. Protein, specifically animal protein, was health. Health was protein. Unfortunately, we believed what had been told to us over and over, and it had been a falsehood.

But Where Do You Get Your Protein? The Protein Stereotype

A truth's initial commotion is directly proportional to how deeply the lie was believed. It wasn't the world being round that agitated people, but that the world wasn't flat. When a well-packaged web of lies has been sold gradually to the masses over generations, the truth will seem utterly preposterous and its speaker a raving lunatic.
- Dresden James

"Where do you get your protein?" is without a doubt the question most asked by those curious about a plant-based diet and one's health. Some of us have an incorrect stereotype of the lean vegetarian or vegan embedded in our craniums from our cultural roots and advertising. As a young man I remember the magazine ads for body building by Joe Weider. Real men built their physique back then with barbells and protein from animal sources. When we think about men who only eat vegetables we might falsely envision the frail standard 98-pound weakling with no energy, strength, or endurance getting sand kicked in their faces on the beach by "real" men who eat meat.

Building Muscle in the Animal Kingdom

If we think about this, many species from the animal kingdom refute this false stereotype. Elephants, rhinos, and hippopotamus are herbivores which build huge muscles and bodies through the same genetic processes as do we humans. Great apes, an example closer to our own species, are omnivores who primarily eat plant foods. They have prodigious, muscular builds. If there wasn't enough protein in plant sources, these plant-eaters would not be able to grow muscle. Many people ignore these examples, since they are non-human animals and humans are different in their eyes. But we see many examples in the human species if we choose to not keep our heads in the sand.

Baboumian: World Record Strength

Vegan athlete Patrik Baboumian is a psychologist and body builder who shatters the weak plant-eater stereotype just as he does world records. In September 2013, Baboumian showed the entire audience at the Harbourfront Centre, in Toronto, Canada, that to be strong, men don't need to eat meat. A vegan since 2011, he broke the heaviest yoke carry world record by carrying 1,100 pounds, 33 feet on his shoulders.[29] He did this while wearing a T-shirt that read: I am a Vegan Badass. In addition, Baboumian holds world records for log lifts and overhead beer keg lifts.

Two years later, and still a vegan, he broke his own heaviest yoke carry world record on September 20, 2015, by carrying more weight in less time, an additional 11 pounds in 28 seconds, than in his previous 2013 world record.[30] Baboumian's feats of strength clearly show a person can perform at world-record levels for multiple years when eating a vegan diet. After 4 years of eating nothing but plants and plant protein, his abilities and power are increasing, not decreasing. Where does one of the strongest men in the world get his protein?

Roll and Lester: Endurance

I heard Rich Roll tell his story a few years ago. It was compelling, motivational, and heartfelt. Roll had an issue with alcohol and drugs which affected his family life and career as an attorney. When he got his addictions under control, he found he was so overweight and out of shape he could hardly get up a flight of stairs. He was on his way to heart disease or some other common debilitating disease caused by an unhealthy, animal-protein-based diet and lifestyle. Roll turned to a vegan diet and athletic performance to help turn his life around.

A swimmer in college, he began swimming again and got involved with Ironman triathlon and Ultraman competitions. He was very successful, and his attainments led him to try something never attempted, called the Epic5[31]. Iron Man triathlons consist of a grueling 2.4-mile swim, a 112-mile bicycle ride, and a marathon run of 26.2 miles, raced in that order with no break.[32] Swim, cycle, and run–no break. His triumph in these races led to an impossible idea. He, along with fellow vegan athlete Jason P. Lester[33], decided they would attempt five full "Iron distance" triathlons on five Hawaiian Islands, in 5 days. Roll was 44 at the time, and he and Lester finished the Epic5 in 7 days.[34] Even though they did not complete the five Ironmans in 5 days as planned, they did succeed in something which had never been done by anyone, let alone by two vegans. The two cycled 560 miles, swam 12 miles, and ran 131 miles. Roll documented his story in the book, _Finding Ultra_. Lester documented his story in _Running on Faith_. Where did Roll and Lester get their protein? They prove plants alone can provide all the energy needed to fuel an epic challenge in endurance.

Oakes: Endurance

Fiona Oakes has been called the "Queen of Extreme" for her feats of endurance competing in more than 50 marathons and ultra-marathons. She is another person who destroys the stereotype that a vegan diet is not an adequate source of nutrition. To point out this fallacy, she ran seven marathons on seven continents in 7 days—and did so in a cow costume. The costume was worn in an act of compassion to bring awareness to animal suffering. She is also a vegan athlete frustrated by being told vegans are weak and cannot perform as well as athletes who eat animals. Her accomplishments prove this is erroneous. As a side note, Oakes also runs a farm sanctuary in Essex, UK, where she cares for 400 animals.[35]

Williams: Healing Power Athleticism

Venus and Serena Williams are powerhouses of athleticism. For decades, the sisters have dominated professional tennis. A few years ago Venus was diagnosed with Sjögren's syndrome, a debilitating autoimmune disease that is, at this point in time, incurable. One symptom is excessive fatigue, and as a consequence she stopped competing. Her doctors recommended a plant-based raw vegan diet. Eating a plant-based diet helped bring the disease into check, and happily she is back on the tennis court, competing at high levels, and winning. She ended 2015 in the top ten of women's tennis for the first time in many years, closing out the year in November with a WTA win in Zhuhai, China. It would seem a vegan diet can put an incurable disease into remission and help an athlete get back into world-class competitive shape.[36]

Du Plessis and Morris: Vegan Body Builders

There are many vegan body builders helping to eradicate the idea that to build muscle you must eat protein from animal sources. Indeed, even the words "vegan body building" seem like an oxymoron taken on their own. But Mr. Universe Barny Du Plessis is a vegan body builder who is showing us we are all wrong about a vegan diet and building muscle.[37] He is a vegan holding the same prestigious award formerly held by the likes of Arnold Schwarzenegger and Lou Ferrigno. Becoming Mr. Universe is a huge accomplishment in the world of body builders. To have a vegan become Mr. Universe is inspirational. There is an excellent interview with Barney here: youtube.com/watch?v=v5K6IKmL_Oo

The late Jim Morris, who passed away at 80 years old, was a lifetime body builder.[38] He broke many stereotypes by having a phenomenal physique his entire life, and he ate a vegan diet. He proved you don't have to deteriorate when you get old.[39] The story of this 80-year-old vegan bodybuilder in a short film can be found here: youtube.com/watch?v=tUtv4slpm-U

It seems like a day cannot go by when we don't hear about vegan athletes performing at world-class levels, whether body builders, tennis players, NFL players, runners, triathletes, or even cage fighters who participate in ultimate fighting challenges[40]. The old stereotype of needing animal products in the world of competitive sports is being replaced with the factual knowledge that a vegan diet is healthier and can make one more competitive (rather than less) in their chosen sport.

Plant Protein Is Superior

Why bring up such a mundane, silly topic such as Guinness World Records for lifting, Ironman competitors, marathon runners, and body builders? Who cares if someone has the record for the heaviest yoke carry over 10 meters? I am always searching for my own stereotyping, my own cultural baggage and blind spots. I used to believe that eating plants made you weak. Buddhists, as inner and outer scientists, seek the truth wherever it is found, and Baboumian's record-breaking feat as a vegan, as do other vegan athletes, helps to break down the stereotype that to be strong and healthy you must eat meat, that you must eat protein from an animal's body. This is utterly wrong and I thank him and all others for helping to show the world this important lesson. These men and women bodybuilders, cyclists, swimmers, tennis players, runners, and other athletes who compete at world-class levels without the "benefit" of eating animal products show us clearly that protein from animals is not necessary.

Where Do You Get Your Fiber?
The Real Deficiency

We are deficient in fiber, not protein, in the U.S. Eating a diet high in fiber is important for many reasons: It relieves constipation, helps maintain a healthy weight, and lowers your risk of diabetes, cancer, and heart disease. "Where do you get your fiber?" is the question vegans need to ask in response to the protein question, as the annual estimated expenditure on prescription laxatives in the United States is $800 million—that's in addition to what we spend on OTC laxative preparations. Michael Greger,

M.D. and author of *How Not To Die*, informs us that the only nutrient Americans are deficient in is fiber. Approximately 97% of Americans do not get enough fiber, and only those who are not eating enough calories every day are deficient in protein. So almost everyone gets enough protein...and vegans and vegetarians get 70% more protein than needed every day. [41] [42] [43] [44] [45]

Appendix A: An Interview with a Vegan Buddhist Nutritionist

About Appendix A, B, and C

There are 3 appendices in the back of the book, each contains an extensive interview with professionals in their field. Two interviews are related to nutritional science: Sherry Morgado and T. Colin Campbell, PhD. The third interview is related to the environment and sustainability with Dr. Richard Oppenlander.

Originally all 3 interviews were incorporated into the main book but they are so very far-reaching I decided to allow readers their choice to delve into them or not. At one point each interview was cut to 75% of its original size for readability and space but they contain such a wealth of information that each are published in their entirety.

Appendix A

Appendix A consists of the talk with Sherry Morgado who is a Buddhist practitioner in the Thich Nhat Hahn Zen lineage. She practices with the Slowly Ripening Sangha at Sky Creek Dharma Center in Chico, California. A vegan for close to a decade and also a nutritionist, Morgado is a Dharma Voices for Animals Board member and loves sharing the Buddha's message of compassion for animals through her example of living peacefully, joyfully, and by not supporting their suffering in her personal life.

Sherry addresses the importance of protein and demystifies the role of protein. She explains how it is metabolized, and even created by our own bodies. She points out that as long as we are eating enough calories from a variety of plant-based sources we will not become protein deficient. In fact she even apprises us that our bodies can make most of the amino acids that it needs. We actually have the biochemical processes inherent in our systems that can make amino acids. "Your body is a protein-making factory," according to Sherry.

All protein needs are available from plant sources. There is no need to eat complete proteins which are generally considered to be from animal sources. Morgado educates us by reminding us our protein needs are much lower than what most people think and we consume too much protein generally in the U.S. The average adult needs about 55-70 grams of protein daily.

Vitamin B12 is needed as a supplement and should be taken everyday. She explains that we generally all need to supplement with B12 whether we eat a plant-based diet or more standard diet due to depletion of soil bacteria.

In addition to educating us on protein and B12 she also demystifies calcium. Calcium is mineral, it comes from the ground, from plants and we can get all we require from plants which include other nutrients required for bone health like, potassium, vitamin C and K. Calcium from plants is more bioavailable (absorbable) than from dairy too, which she elucidates.

Morgado is a strong proponent of self education and suggests a few good reference books:

- *Vegan for Life* by Jack Norris and Virginia Messina

- *Becoming Vegan* by Brenda Davis and Vesanto Melina
- *Never Too Late to Go Vegan* by Carol J. Adams, Patti Breitman, and Virginia Messina

Please take the time to read the entire interview, I guarantee you will learn something new.

Campbell, Furhman, Barnard, and Esselstyn

If you've read _The Buddha, The Vegan, and You: Part 1,_ you know that my vegan voyage began with a 30-day challenge from my wife in 2010. At that juncture I began reading about veganism. These four books had a tremendous impact on my understanding of nutrition as I began this journey:

1. _The China Study_ by T. Colin Campbell, PhD and Thomas M. Campbell II
2. _Eat to Live_ by Joel Fuhrman MD
3. _Dr. Neal Barnard's Program for Reversing Diabetes_ by Neal D. Barnard MD
4. _Prevent and Reverse Heart Disease_ by Caldwell B. Esselstyn, Jr., MD

The same message came through from each of these books. Eating animal products is associated with obesity and the diseases we consider common: heart disease, diabetes, and various cancers. Elimination of animal products from your diet in favor of a WFPB diet, low in oil, is associated with a suspension, reversal, or prevention of these and other diseases.

A brief summary of the most important points I learned from each book follows; however, please note: If you have a chronic disease, before altering anything please consult with your physician. What may seem like a simple diet change can cause quick and intense differences which should be monitored. In other words, do not underestimate the strong effect going on a simple

WFPB diet can have on your bodily functions. Consult your health-care provider.

The China Study

I had the good fortune to attend a few presentations given by T. Colin Campbell, PhD,[46] in the past few years and a chance to briefly speak with him twice. I told him he was one of my heroes, and when I run across someone who is interested in improving their health I give them a copy of *The China Study*[47]. I mentioned that it was my wife who initially got me to take the vegan challenge for 30 days and eating a plant-based diet. He stated with a smirk and a nod toward his wife Karen that he eats everything she tells him to eat, also.

Dr. Campbell didn't always advocate a plant-based diet, as he was raised on a dairy farm and grew up eating the Standard American Diet (SAD). He believed, as most of us, that a diet laden with meat, dairy, and eggs was the finest in the world. In fact, the initial focus in the early years of his career was finding ways to produce better types of animal protein in order to feed the world's starving population. He found himself in the Philippines, studying liver cancer, and later the project director of *The China Study*, which lasted over 20 years. This study is considered one of the most comprehensive ever conducted on nutrition and was a partnership involving two universities, Cornell and Oxford, and the Chinese Academy of Preventative Medicine.

I struggled through the book the first time I read it. It is full of data, statistics, and facts that present a view of food very contrary to what I'd been led to believe. Reading it can make one feel like Neo in *The Matrix*. If you want to stay in a reality governed by false information and ignorance, then don't read _The China Study_. But if you want to wake up and open your eyes and take the red pill, then read it! Be warned, you will probably never look at food the same way again.

A graduate from Cornell with an MS and PhD in nutrition and biochemistry, Dr. Campbell's essential message is that there is a link between eating animal-based proteins and the development of Western diseases of affluence such as cancer, heart disease, and diabetes. Casein, the major protein found in milk and cheese, is considered to be "a chemical carcinogen, perhaps the most relevant carcinogen that we consume," according to Dr. Campbell[48]. He found that at the cellular level animal foods can turn cancer on and plant foods can turn cancer off.

Much of what Dr. Campbell uncovers in _The China Study_ and continues to elaborate upon in his second book, _Whole: Rethinking the Science of Nutrition_, points to a view of nutrition that has been narrowly constricted by the process of scientific reductionism. Scientific reductionism focuses the attention of researchers very intently upon single nutrients. Doing so takes the nutrients out of the natural context in which they exist. It is simplistic thinking with the motive to market and sell rather than looking at nutrients in the complex fashion in which they exist and provide nutrition.

Furthermore, studies based on single nutrient analysis lead to confusion and conflicting results. Dr. Campbell shows that by eating whole foods, close to their natural state, we allow nature and our bodies to sort out what is needed (as they have for millions of years) and what is to be discarded. Dr. Campbell informs us the closer we can get to eating a whole-foods plant-based diet (WFPB) the healthier we will be.

Essential Points from *The China Study*

- America is sick. One-third of adults 20 and over are obese, and the number of overweight Americans far exceeds those with a healthy weight. The number of people with diabetes (one in 13 Americans) has inflated to unprecedented proportions, and those who suffer from it have many of its secondary results: kidney disease, cardiovascular disease, limb amputation, blindness, stroke, and other ailments up to and including an early untimely death. Diabetes and obesity are indicators of our country's generalized deficient health, and neither condition occurs in isolation, rather they predict we will have other serious health issues with our population, namely: heart disease, cancers, and strokes.

- Obesity is the forerunner of bad health, causing many Americans to become disabled and putting our health-care system under tremendous stress. We pay more for health care than any other nation in the world. Yet in spite of paying more, we have worse health. The prescription for good health is: Eat plants, which provide myriad benefits versus animal-based foods, which are correlated with health dangers.

- Animal protein stimulates cancer growth, whereas plant protein does not. In a laboratory simulation with rats, liver cancer foci in the animals exposed to high doses of aflatoxin increased and enlarged when fed a

20% animal-protein diet and they receded when animal protein was reduced to 5% of the diet. Cancer foci growth, it was found, could be reversed based solely on animal protein rats ate. The animal protein used was casein, a milk protein which makes up 87% of cow's milk. What about plant protein? Plant protein did not stimulate cancer progression at all, whether at low levels or high levels.

- The China Study data consisted of a survey of 880 million people in 2,400 counties and, when completed, showed who was dying of what and where. The study took into account 12 different types of cancer in China, and surveyed lifestyle factors to correlate what people died from with their environment, including the food they ate.

- Cancer was higher in populations who ate more animal protein and lower in populations who ate less animal protein. It was almost nonexistent in those populations who ate an almost 100% plant-based diet. Data mapping showed clearly that as consumption of animal-based foods went up, so did breast cancer rates. This was true of all types of cancers mapped. The results of the study showed a correlation between human consumption of animal-based foods and the rat and mice experiments in the laboratory.

- We have a myopic view of genetics. While genetics and our family background play a part in cancer initiation within our bodies, focusing all our attention on genetics takes us off the hook for having any responsibility or ability to affect this disease. Initiation is only one part of getting disease. Once the disease is initiated, what is more important is whether our body will allow it to be promoted and grow. Looking only at genetics is fatalistic and a form of denial. We become very limited in our ability to respond and ignore the point that genes need to become expressed for them to promote an initiated cancer.

- "Normal" cholesterol levels put us all at risk for heart disease. The study correlated consumption factors of animal-based foods with cholesterol levels, showing a link between cholesterol eaten and cholesterol in the blood. Heart patients who follow the government recommendation with regard to cholesterol levels are at risk for heart attack, as we know the 35% of Americans with cholesterol levels between 150 mg/dL and 200 mg/dL are stricken by heart attacks. The recommended blood cholesterol level of 200 mg/dL is not safe. The 30% low-fat diet is unhealthy and unsafe, and thousands of Americans could be saved the trauma and cost of experiencing heart disease by switching to a whole-foods plant-based diet.

- We can for the most part eliminate type 2 diabetes with diet and have much better control of type 1 diabetes through eating a WFPB diet.

- When compared to other populations in the world, America has one of the highest consumptions of dairy per person. Yet we do not have strong bones. American women over 50 have one of the greatest hip fracture rates in the world, with only two countries ahead of us, Australia and New Zealand, whose populations consume more milk than

Americans. Hip fractures are a sign of osteoporosis. Research from Yale School of Medicine explains that 70% of these hip fractures are attributable to animal protein consumption. Our bodies are alkaline. Consumption of animal protein, including dairy, creates an acidic condition. To neutralize the acidic condition caused by animal protein, the body pulls the alkaline calcium from the bones, weakening them.

Appendix B: An Interview with T. Colin Campbell

I had some further conversation with Dr. Campbell around these topics in 2016. I asked him about the paleo diet and his response was how easy it is to justify our bad habits. According to Dr. Campbell, "people like to hear good things about their bad habits." He goes on to explain how patently ridiculous the paleo diet is, as it's a diet based around fat and protein and when one compares populations of people over a lifetime, anyone on a diet like this has a much higher risk of cancer, heart disease and other diseases. He talks about his debates with Loren Cordain and knowing Boyd Eaton, the father of the paleo movement, who is now "coming over to our side".

Our discussion also led to the new USDA food pyramid info, which now mentions plant-based foods and while on the surface this gives the appearance of being directionally correct Dr. Campbell tells us it's the same old "spinning wheel" with the USDA making up fancy reports with a lot a data without any real change at all. The USDA is still subject to the whims of the livestock industry.

Dr. Campbell feels very strongly that what is going to make the true change occur is a bottom-up approach. Having worked on congressional committees and expert panels for decades he sees little change. But the bottom up approach as portrayed in the movie, *Plant Pure Nation*, has great potential.

Please take time to read the entire interview and also read *The China Study* and *Whole: Rethinking the Science of Nutrition* for all the details. Links for more information about Dr. Campbell's work, the Cornell Nutrition course, and to purchase his books are provided here:

The China Study book:
   benbellavegan.com/book/the-china-study/
Whole: Rethinking the Science of Nutrition:
   nutritionstudies.org/whole/
Center for Nutrition Studies eCornell:
   nutritionstudies.org

Eat to Live: Joel Fuhrman, MD

Dr. Joel Fuhrman[49] is a very renowned medical doctor who specializes in preventing and reversing disease through nutrition. He is known for his focus on a "micronutrient-rich diet," which consists of low-fat plant-based whole-foods, and contains zero (or extremely low) consumption of animal products. He introduces a health formula in his book *Eat to Live* where H=N/C (Health = Nutrients/Calories) and tells patients and readers alike when the ratio of nutrients to calories is high then a person's health is high and if overweight, weight loss will naturally occur. H=N/C is achieved through eating lots of green leafy plants and eliminating oil, animal products, and processed foods.

Dr. Fuhrman has appeared on *Dr. Oz, The Today Show, Good Morning America,* and PBS stations, to name a few. He is not a vegan but wholly endorses a completely plant-based diet for optimal health. His 6-week plan for weight loss prescribes no animal products, no dairy, no between-meal snacking, no fruit juice, and no oil. According to Dr. Fuhrman we should all be eating healthy salads every day as our main meals. If we follow these dietary recommendations, we will not need to worry about carrying a sack of medication around with us for the rest of our lives. He believes we can in many cases reverse disease with diet and can prevent heart disease and cancer without the use of drugs by eating a WFPB diet, high in micronutrients and low in fat, and that by doing so we create super immunity within our bodies.

Important Themes from *Eat to Live*

- Obesity. Americans are killing themselves using forks, knives, and spoons. We eat a high-calorie diet that is nutrient deficient. Obesity is our number one health problem, and it is increasing so fast that if trends continue, all Americans will be obese by 2048. Obesity complications are associated with the following diseases: adult onset diabetes, cancer, hypertension, degenerative arthritis, coronary heart disease, and more.

- Due to the fact that we eat high-calorie foods that are nutrient deficient, we eat too much and are still not nourished. We are addicted to eating in a toxic manner and are always in a state of hunger, which Dr. Fuhrman defines as "toxic hunger." This is why we overconsume, since our natural ability to feel full is overridden and we are in a condition of incessant hunger. But when we eat a WFPB, high-nutrient, and low-calorie diet, the symptoms of toxic hunger disappear. Nutrient-rich whole foods are high in fiber and fill us up. Fiber is critical to good health and needs to be eaten in a whole-food format to protect against disease. Eating nutrient-rich foods that are low in calories increases lifespan, prevents chronic disease, and helps us lose unnecessary weight.

- Phytochemicals are extraordinary for health, and humans are built on biological systems that require a high intake of natural and unprocessed plant-derived foods, such as fruits and vegetables. On the other hand, cancer is a disease caused by a shortage of fruits and vegetables. Without these types of food, we get cancer, a "disease of maladaptation," because we are not feeding the body the complex compounds necessary to protect our bodily systems. A single tomato, as an example, contains in excess of 10,000 unique phytochemicals whose synergetic effects we know nothing about. Pills cannot replace fruits and vegetables, as isolated single nutrients do not provide the same protection against disease.

- Protein exists in all foods. The average person needs to consume 10% of their daily calorie consumption in the form of protein. When eating a WFPB diet, all your protein needs are completely met if you consume enough calories. Don't worry about getting enough protein. For example, green leafy vegetables are approximately 50% protein, and broccoli has almost twice as much protein as beef steak per calorie.

- We need carbohydrates. Carbohydrates are necessary for our entire biological system to run on, including muscles and brain cells. Unrefined carbs in the form of WFPB foods encourage weight loss since they are low in calories and high in fiber, compared to animal-based foods or processed foods.

- Breaking addictive eating behavior is hard. The first step is the same as breaking any other addiction: recognition of the habit. Sometimes the only thing that can cause recognition and motivation to change is disease, fear, and pain. Knowing the scientific data and research is not convincing for many people. The human mind has great abilities to rationalize and justify deep-rooted habits.

- Good health can be predicted. A healthy diet and lifestyle predicts good health in the future. If you eat a SAD, you will get the same diseases most Americans get. Going to see doctors, homeopaths, acupuncturists, and other health professionals and getting treatments from them does not make you healthy, it only relieves symptoms. In general, physicians have little experience treating disease naturally from a nutritional perspective. Foods are the cure, but patients are told nutrition has nothing to do with health.

- Heart disease is the number one killer in the U.S., with a death every 30 seconds—each of which could be avoided. If you are over 40 you have a 90% chance of having atherosclerosis, and an Americanized low-fat diet does not provide much assistance. Studies show a majority of patients with coronary disease who follow the American Heart Association recommendations see their conditions worsen. No studies show reversal or halting of disease for those following the recommendations. Contrary to this, there is a lot of evidence showing the majority of patients on a plant-based, micronutrient-rich diet reverse their heart disease.

Please read *Eat to Live* for detailed information and refer to Dr. Fuhrman's website and blog:

Dr. Fuhrman's website: drfuhrman.com/

Dr. Fuhrman's blog: diseaseproof.com/

Dr. Neal Barnard's Program for Reversing Diabetes

Neal D. Barnard, MD, is a well-known advocate for health through nutritional excellence. He is a researcher and author of 12 books, and much of his research has been done on the function of nutrition in treating diabetes and obesity and the management of lipids. He is also the president of PCRM, Physicians Committee for Responsible Medicine, a nonprofit (which anyone can join) founded in 1985 with more than 12,000 participating doctors.[50]

Dr. Barnard is an advocate for a vegan low-fat diet due to its ability to promote health and well-being. He was not raised as a vegan but born into a family of North Dakota cattle ranchers. He, like most of us, was raised on a meat and potatoes diet, where bacon and egg breakfasts dripping with grease in the morning were more the norm. But not today. After many years of study, research, and practice, he shows clearly that we can reverse or halt many of the diseases we believe are common. One of his books, entitled *Dr. Neal Barnard's Program for Reversing Diabetes,* published in 2007, highlights research findings that show a new, successful approach to the treatment of diabetes is more effective than medication in many instances. The approach is simple to follow and is found to be helpful in types 1 and 2 of the disease.

Key pieces of information from Dr. Neal Barnard's Program for Reversing Diabetes are:

- Food is powerful in prevention and treatment of diabetes. Food can in many cases reverse trends. Many people can lower or eliminate medication after a few weeks on a vegan low-fat diet.

- Genes do not predetermine your fate in getting diabetes. Just because you may have a genetic predisposition toward diabetes, since it may run in your family, it does not mean you will get the disease.

- Fat is a big problem for persons with diabetes. Insulin cannot unlock cells to let glucose in when there is too much fat in a person's body. But fat inside our cells is not everlasting. When we stop ingesting fat, the fat inside our cells starts to vanish. This is shown by researchers from the Imperial College School of Medicine, who measured calf muscle fat in vegans and omnivores. Vegans, it turns out, have 31% less fat in their muscles than omnivores.

- Saturated fat is linked to insulin resistance and heart disease, so avoid animal products as they contain saturated fat. Additionally, diets high in animal protein can exacerbate kidney difficulties and lead to calcium loss; and as they do not have fiber or healthy carbohydrates, we should avoid them, especially if one has diabetes.

- Avoid all foods high in fat, including foods containing vegetable oils. A gram of carbohydrates is 4 calories. A gram of olive oil, corn oil, or bacon grease is 9 calories. We should avoid (or severely limit) foods fried in oil. We should shoot for no more than a few grams of fat per serving of food we eat. The amount of fat we need in our diet is very small. We can get all the fat we need from a vegan diet.

- Eat low on the glycemic index. The glycemic index categorizes food that raises our blood sugar rapidly. We should use this index to learn about better foods to eat and shift our palate toward them. Some examples of foods we should be eating are: beans, green leafy vegetables, fresh fruit, pasta (cooked al dente), pumpernickel or rye bread, sweet potatoes, oatmeal, and bran cereal.

- Eat a high-fiber diet. We should be eating 40 grams of fiber per day from sources like beans, fruits, whole grain, and vegetables. The goal we should have in mind is to eat at least 10 grams of fiber per meal.

- Plant protein is all you need. A diet consisting of beans, vegetables, fruits, and grains provide all the protein your body needs. Period.

- Calcium is better for us from sources such as green leafy vegetables as it has higher absorption and retention rates than from dairy. Romaine lettuce, broccoli, and beans, as examples, are a better source of calcium than dairy products, as evidenced by the results of the Nurse's Health Study conducted by Harvard University. Milk-drinking participants in the study showed no greater defense from fractures than non-milk drinkers, putting aside the myth that dairy builds stronger bones than vegetables.

- Diabetes is not caused by carbohydrates. Powerful evidence exists to show the opposite, that complex carbohydrates actually prevent the disease. In countries such as Japan, China, and Thailand, and many parts of Africa, where diabetes is unknown, the population eats a diet heavy in carbohydrates from whole-food sources. These populations eat more carbohydrates than we do and yet have no diabetes. It's not until these groups adopt a Western diet that the disease appears. As pointed out, when Japanese people move from their traditional diets heavy in rice and plant-based whole-foods to one characterized by animal products and high fat, their genetic proclivity toward diabetes awakens.

- Numerous studies show the positive effect of a vegan low-fat diet on diabetes. Studies from the University of Kentucky, University of California, George Washington University School of Medicine, and the University of Toronto in conjunction with the PCRM are reviewed.

- A low-fat vegan diet is the best for people with diabetes and is easy to follow. Despite the belief that a vegan plant-based low-fat diet is difficult to embrace, Dr. Barnard's research shows evidence to the contrary. When people with diabetes are educated and properly introduced to this way of eating, most find it is gratifying and uncomplicated to follow.

Please read *Dr. Neal Barnard's Program for Reversing Diabetes* for details. Additional information about Dr. Neal D. Barnard, to purchase his books, and to learn more about PCRM, Physicians Committee for Responsible Medicine, can be found at the following links:

Dr. Neal D. Barnard: nealbarnard.org/
Physicians Committee for Responsible Medicine: pcrm.org/

Prevent and Reverse Heart Disease

Caldwell B. Esselstyn, Jr., MD, spent time in Vietnam as an Army surgeon in 1967 and then joined the famed Cleveland Clinic in 1968. During his career as a surgeon at

Cleveland Clinic, he rose to many leadership positions, including president of the staff and chairman of the Breast Cancer Task Team, and became a member of the Board of Governors. In 2000, he gave up his position at Cleveland Clinic but continued his work in helping people learn to overcome heart disease. In 2005 he was the first recipient of the Benjamin Spock Award for Compassion in Medicine. He, along with Dean Ornish and T. Colin Campbell, recently persuaded former U.S. President Bill Clinton to adopt a largely plant-based diet.

In his book, *Prevent and Reverse Heart Disease*, Dr. Esselstyn confronts orthodox symptom-treating cardiology practices. He believes coronary heart disease doesn't need to exist and that if you have it you can stop its progression. He describes in easy-to-understand terminology how the disease works, and shows us clearly how we, our families, and communities can live our lives without coronary heart disease through a plant-based diet, a diet he has followed personally for more than 30 years.

Highlights from Prevent and Reverse Heart Disease

- Coronary heart disease is the leading killer of adults in the U.S., where 500,000 men and women die from heart disease annually. Also, 1.5 million people have heart attacks but do not die and another 3 million people have silent heart attacks and never know it.

- We spend $250 billion annually to treat heart disease, but most of this money goes toward the treatment of symptoms and not curing the principal cause of the disease. Hospitals are "cathedrals of sickness" rather than of health.

- The medical profession has an attachment to the mechanical treatment of symptoms, and the root cause for this is money and the belief that his diet-change ideas are too "radical" to be embraced by the general public. However, most of the world (73%) consumes a plant-based diet, and in those cultures heart disease is unknown.

- Mappings of disease incidence around the world show chronic disorders crowded into Western societies, like the EU and the U.S. The reason is diet. Where a diet was primarily plant-based and thus low in fat and cholesterol but high in nutrition, chronic disease was for the most part nonexistent.

- In the U.S. we consume on average 65 pounds of fat annually. We have cholesterol levels that hover at 200 mg/dL. There is no doubt we eat our way to heart disease. Those countries where this disease is unknown have diets low in fat and cholesterol levels below 150 mg/dL.

- To see if a change in diet could be helpful in U.S. patients with advanced stages of coronary heart disease, Dr. Esselstyn simulated the diet of countries that do not have an issue with the disease. Of the 24 patients who stayed with the program, 18 achieved remarkable results which showed their heart disease progression had been halted. Eight of the eighteen even showed reversal of the disease in their angiogram results. Over the five years on a plant-based diet the supply of blood through the coronary arteries to their hearts had improved. Dr. Esselstyn's patients had become "heart attack–proof," whereas the patients who had dropped out showed a progression of disease.

- The mechanical or surgical approach through angioplasty, stents, and bypass procedures relieves the patient of the symptoms but does nothing for the underlying disease. We are informed a better approach is by going to the basis of the sickness and cutting off its fat and cholesterol supply. If we follow a plant-based diet with no-oil, one's body cannot deposit fat and cholesterol into our arteries.

- In opposition to the American Heart Association doctrine, we learn that moderation kills. Research shows if you have heart disease, then any amount of fat in your diet will continue to progress the disease.

- Nitric oxide and the endothelium play a big role in artery health. Nitric oxide is a chemical compound manufactured by the endothelium cells in our artery linings, and it is a Teflon-like compound which, among other things, makes the linings of our arteries smooth and slippery and facilitates dilation when necessary. Smooth and slippery arteries are a good thing because they become a pathway where plaque has a hard time building up.

- In one telling experiment, Dr. Vogel, University of Maryland School of Medicine, found a great decrease in endothelium cell function for up to 6 hours after college students ate a fast-food breakfast. The argument is made that if one single meal of fast food has a measurable 6-hour effect on young college students' arteries, what effect does it have on those of us who eat three meals high in fat, on a daily basis for years? We are harming our endothelium by eating damaging foods.

- Corporate interests are in direct opposition to the benefits of a plant-based diet. Those who make dietary recommendations in the USDA are made up of former employees of the meat and dairy industry. Dr. Esselstyn informs us "the fox is in the hen house," causing us to get compromised guidelines, watered-down truth, and inaccurate recommendations, which actually cause disease. He feels the USDA is so compromised they should disqualify themselves from setting nutrition standards.

- If you never want to develop heart disease, some simple steps are suggested: Do not eat any products that come from animals, eliminate all oils and refined grain products, and avoid all nuts (if you have heart disease). If you do not have heart disease you can eat walnuts, in moderation.

Prevent and Reverse Heart Disease contains a plethora of information left out of this short review. Please purchase the book for more information. To learn more about Dr. Caldwell B. Esselstyn please visit his website[51].

dresselstyn.com/site/

Are We Designed to Eat Meat?

Let a person not give power to the many rationalizations given to justify animal flesh eating. What logicians say under the influence of their addictive craving for animal flesh is sophistic, delusional, and argumentative. What they imagine that they witnessed, heard, or suspected that the Blessed One has said, or another Buddha said or did, is grossly distorted.

As greed is a hindrance to liberation, so are the objects of greed a hindrance to liberation. Objects of greed like animal flesh eating and consuming alcohol are hindrances to liberation.

A time may come when deluded people may say, 'Animal flesh is appropriate food to eat, has no karmic consequences, and is permitted by the Buddha.'

Some will even say that eating animal flesh can be medicinal. It is more like eating the flesh of your only child. Let a yogi be attuned to what is balanced and nourishing to eat, be adverse to consuming animal flesh and alcohol, and with this clarity go about peacefully begging for food, trusting that what is wanted and needed to sustain a healthy life will be supplied.

Animal flesh eating is forbidden by me everywhere and for all time for those who abide in compassion.

The Buddha, Mahaparinirvana Sutra

Tibetan Buddhism teaches that being a human is a wonderful gift, as we can achieve anything we wish, including total awakening. We were not born into the many realms possible: god, hell, hungry ghost, or animal. There are many realms of existence according to most forms of Buddhism. The human realm and animal realm exist on this earth. God realms exist in heavenly places, and hell realms exist in miserable places. Then there is the hungry ghost realm, represented by extreme lack and a constant irritation of deep craving that can never be satisfied. All of these other realms of existence come with conditions not conducive to awakening. In god realms we have no reason to practice, as everything seems so perfect and wonderful, until it is too late and death arrives. In hell realms we are tortured, suffer, and feel such pain that we cannot find the peace of mind to practice. The hungry ghost realm consumes each and every moment with looking for food and drink, while in the animal realm, a realm we can actually verify and see here and now, we are continually looking over our shoulder, worried we will be captured and eaten by another animal—alive. All of these realms of life are impermanent, and we die and are reborn over and over again up and down the sequence based on our karmic inclination.

While this is an interesting cosmology to ponder, there seems to be a pedestal that humans are put upon that doesn't fit or isn't deserving unless we look closely at our true nature and not what we have become and done collectively to the earth, the animals, and ourselves. Psychologically, anatomically, biologically, and biochemically we are not carnivorous killers but altruistic herbivorous-frugivores who easily are able to exhibit cooperation and live compassionately.

However, we are part of the animal realm, and while we don't generally eat animals while they are alive, we clearly do eat animals, and we eat them to the tune of 70 billion land animals and close to 3 trillion sea animals per year. Generally, we kill and cook animals before we eat them. And we generally pay others to kill them for us, as we like them cleaned and prepared in a non-natural condition, without all the guts and gore. This tells us two things about ourselves: 1) animals are not our natural food, and 2) we psychologically do not like to kill living beings.

This makes us different from carnivores that must kill by their very nature. Killing is not part of our innate nature and psychological makeup. As we are not carnivores, we justify, deny, and obscure the truth of killing wherever we are involved in these deadly acts. True carnivores do not deny or obscure but guard, gorge, and protect their precious kill.

Dr. Douglas Graham supplies a cogent argument for why we are not carnivores in his book, _The 80-10-10 Diet,_ where he states, "Our anatomy, physiology, biochemistry, and psychology all indicate we are not carnivores."[52] I, and others, could not agree with him more.

Anatomy, Physiology, and Biochemistry of a Carnivore

Anatomically, we differ from carnivores in many ways. We walk on two legs and have no tails. We also have no rough, raspy tongues for licking up blood and gore. Our tongues are smooth and velvety. We don't have claws but smooth, flat nails ideal for peeling fruit. Our hands, with opposable thumbs, are ideally equipped for picking and peeling fruit, not tearing apart live animals. Carnivores, who do not have opposable thumbs, have claws perfect for catching an animal by digging into flesh (as anyone who has ever had a cat in their arms when it panics knows). Claws like these are made for the ripping open of flesh, not the peeling of an orange or banana. And we, normally, have one offspring at birth rather than the litter common with carnivores. These coincide with the multiple sets of teats we see on natural carnivores as opposed to the two supplied by nature to human mothers.

We don't drink by lapping up water, but have this unique ability to use our lips to sip and suck water because our tongues do not stick out far enough for us to enable lapping up of water. We are sippers, not lappers.

My friend Chris, an avid Michigan deer hunter with diabetes—and a self-proclaimed carnivore—is quick to point out we have carnivorous canine teeth designed to rip flesh. He points to his teeth and states, "If we were not meant to eat meat, why do we all have canine teeth?" But Ashley Capps, activist and writer, makes an excellent argument against this justification, as she points out that some of the largest canine teeth grow in the mouths of 100% herbivores.[53] The hippo, saber-toothed deer,

Gelada baboon, camel, and javelina all have huge canine teeth yet are plant eaters. Thus canine teeth in and of themselves do not make us meat-eaters. Additionally, when looking at teeth, scientists who study mammals use a system to describe the layout of all the teeth in an animal's mouth called the dental formula. This formula provides vital indications as to the evolutionary background of each animal.[54] This descriptive system counts incisors, canines, premolars, and molars and their overall arrangement. Our dental formula, it turns out, is more like a frugivore[55] than a carnivore, as we don't have a mouth full of canines like carnivores do. Our flat molars are good for squashing and mashing food, not ripping it, and we have side-to-side movement in our jaws so we can break plant cell walls down to unlock the needed nutrients and mix them with our saliva. Carnivores do not have side-to-side movement, i.e., the need to mash. They simply rip and swallow whole.

When we analyze our stomachs we find they are very close anatomically to those of chimpanzees and orangutans. One scientist comments that if we were to sketch out each of the stomachs of various species of monkeys, apes, and humans, we would forget which belonged to whom prior to ever finishing the task, because they are so similar.[56] Our intestines are 12 times the length of our torso, whereas a carnivore's intestines are three times the length of their torsos. Our long intestines allow us to slowly ingest and absorb nutrients from plant-based food, which are high in cellulose, fiber, and fructose. The gastrointestinal region of a carnivore is so much shorter and smoother because it must allow quick, unhindered passage of rotting flesh. Eating the dead body of an animal must be a quick affair or the putrefaction process will hurt health.

Ever wondered why your cat sleeps most of the day? They are a typical carnivore. Carnivores are known to have long sleep patterns of up to 20 hours per day, whereas other than teenagers, most humans sleep only 8 hours per day. [57] [58] [59] [60]

Anatomically, our stomachs can't hold the amount of food a carnivore's can. They are known to eat their entire kill in one sitting, gorging until they can hardly move. Our meal sizes are much smaller, and we eat much more often.

Physiologically, we perspire through our skin, whereas carnivores perspire through their noses. We see in color in order to see fruit and greens and differentiate between ripe, rotten/overripe, and unripe fruits, whereas carnivores do not commonly have a need for color vision.

The biochemistry of carnivores and humans is very different. Biologically we do not, and cannot, manufacture our own vitamin C. Carnivores can. We have to eat food with vitamin C to get what we need to stay healthy; otherwise we get scurvy. [61] [62]

We also have very different microbial tolerances from carnivores, who can withstand microbes in raw carcasses that would make us sick or kill us. Botulism, as an example, is deadly to humans, but carnivores, with high levels of acid in their stomachs, easily handle eating this microorganism.

Strong acid is needed to digest the rotting carcass of the animals that carnivores ingest, and while we can digest meat, it is hard for our bodies to do so. The power of hydrogen (pH) is a measurement of the hydrogen ion concentration in bodies. The total pH scale ranges from 1 to 14, where 7 is considered to be neutral. A pH below 7 is said to be acidic and greater than 7 is alkaline. The level of pH we humans produce in our stomachs ranges 10 - 1,000 times weaker than that of carnivores.[63] Meat is an acid-forming food upon which true carnivores thrive. However, acid-forming foods can cause health problems in humans.[64] Humans have a more alkaline body than carnivores, and generally, plants are an alkaline-forming food.

Our saliva and urine is alkaline,[65] whereas the saliva and urine of a carnivore is acidic. We digest differently than natural meat-eaters, too, and lack uricase, an enzyme that neutralizes uric acid (a waste product) found in all flesh. But we all have the enzyme ptyalin in our saliva, which carnivores do not, whose function is to initiate the digestion of fruits and vegetables. Those enzymes we do have in common with natural meat-eating animals are in very different ratios.

Tolerances for sugar found in fruit are very low in carnivores. Carnivores who eat too much glucose and fructose are very disposed to diabetes. On the other hand, we are prone to disease when we eat a diet predominated by animal products. Our bodies cannot tolerate high-fat and -cholesterol diets. Insulin is locked out of cells in our bodies when we eat a high-fat, animal-product-rich diet and we develop type 2 diabetes.[66] [67] Our cholesterol and triglyceride lipid levels rise when we eat those foods and our arteries get clogged. Carnivores do not get high cholesterol or atherosclerosis from eating meat, ever. Lions and tigers don't have high cholesterol issues, as Sofia Pineda Ochoa, MD, clearly tells us in her short movie, *Are We Omnivores, Carnivores or Herbivores?*[68] In summary, we humans get disease from eating meat, whereas carnivores get disease from eating fruits and vegetables.

When we compare between humans and carnivores, what we see there are differences. Anatomically, the bodily structures between humans and carnivores are different. Physiologically, our bodies function differently. The chemical and physicochemical processes that occur within human bodies are distinctly different. So what about the psychology of humans toward killing?

Psychology of a Carnivore

Mentally and emotionally, we are not true carnivores. We only eat meat due to culture, taste, and attachment to conditioned-historical-survival methods related to bouts of famine. As a species we don't like to kill. We don't like gore and guts or causing others to suffer.

Slaughterhouses don't have glass walls, because we don't like to see animals killed. Slaughterhouses are not found on every corner like convenience stores, because we don't like to kill. We don't install slaughter facilities in our homes, because we don't like to kill. As a consequence, we don't even really know today where our meat comes from, and we don't really want to know, because we don't like to kill animals and really don't want to know (or think) that we are accessories to murder. This informs us of our psychological makeup.

Conscientious Objectors on the Battlefield

We have a picture in our minds, due in part to movies and books, that soldiers during historical conflicts were efficient killers of others, who all bravely fired their weapons at the enemy. However, the research from wartime data clearly shows this is not true. We do not want to kill other humans, even in times of warfare. Unromantically, most soldiers become conscientious objectors at the point they must actually fire their gun to take another's life, a truth for both sides of any given conflict, until perhaps more recent times. [69]

Data collected by Ardant du Picq, via investigations and discussions with French officers in the 1860s, showed many French soldiers had a very high propensity to fire harmlessly above the heads of the enemy. Paddy Griffith, a researcher of Napoleonic and U.S. Civil War, found that hit rates of one or two men per minute during combat on the whole battlefield were the norm (rather than hundreds per minute). This had a high correlation and supports the discoveries of du Picq, since musket technology, accuracy, and the distance between enemy troops should have had kill rates considerably higher than this. The experiences of Lieutenant George Roupell, a commander of a British platoon in World War I, strongly compare with du Picq's and Griffith's findings, as he had to draw his sword and beat his men to get them to stop firing in the air. Lastly, U.S. Army Brigadier General S.L.A. Marshall and his team of researchers found that only 15-20% of American World War II soldiers would participate in killing the enemy using their weapons. In other words, 80-85% of U.S. World War II soldiers at any given time would not fire at the enemy.[70]

The U.S. military took notice of this data, and after World War II they institutionalized Pavlonian-type conditioning to improve rates of killing in Korea and Vietnam. It is only through these recent reconditioning processes, used in modern boot camps, that firing rates have gone up. In other words, firing rates have increased since World War II because we have become adept at desensitizing our troops against their basic nature. But the Pavlovian training comes at a very high cost. When, through continual conditioning, troops learn to deny their basic natural tendencies and learn to glorify killing, Post Traumatic Stress Disorder (PTSD) rates go up along with firing rates. The psychological cost is staggering. While we can be conditioned to deny the truth that we don't want to kill others, when combatants come back from war they realize their victims were not mere targets but humans just like themselves, with needs, wants, and families. This correlates with the PTSD that slaughterhouse workers experience.

In similar fashion, meat eaters desensitize themselves to the truth of suffering of animals through culture and denial that animals actually feel pain and can truly suffer. Psychological testing on the cognitive dissonance associated with eating animals by Steve Loughnan, of Kent University in the U.K. found people who choose to eat meat change their beliefs about animal suffering, intelligence, and moral status. We tell ourselves, "They don't suffer, so I can eat them."[71]

Thus we do the same thing to ourselves as boot camp drill sergeants and training processes. We train ourselves to see animals as less than what they are so we can kill and eat them, just as modern soldiers can shoot and kill with greater rates of precision by seeing the enemy as less than what they are. We don't want to feel guilty about eating animals, just as we don't want to feel guilty about killing other human beings. We must deny our own senses and the feelings, intelligence, and capacity of animals, to psychologically enable us to eat them. We must repress our own innate wisdom of our connection to sentient life in order to eat them. We are not OK with the killing of beings, but we repress this in order to eat them.

We as a species have succeeded because we are collaborators, not killers. Every day, trillions of peaceful transactions take place in a nonviolent manner. What gets into the news is offensive to us, and while we are drawn to it (bad news sells), it is not because we like violence, it is because it's abhorrent. We have an aversion to killing. Killing is repugnant to us and is opposite of our own true nature. This is why violent news, TV shows, and movies draw us in. We are drawn to the opposite of what we truly are. We are empathetic beings with compassionate hearts. We are able, when we don't repress feelings, to put ourselves in the other person's (and the other sentient being's) shoes because we are altruistic and empathetic. This explains the military paradox where studies show soldiers do not want to kill others, even in time of war. When soldiers fire over the heads of others intentionally, we should see this as a part of the natural aversion to killing, which a true carnivore doesn't and cannot have when hungry.

The classic Harvey Diamond example describes this aptly. Give a baby in a playpen an apple and a live rabbit. They will eat the apple and play with the rabbit.[72] Why? Because we are fruit and plant eaters. We are not attracted to gore, guts, and blood. We don't crave these substances. Our saliva ducts don't work on flesh foods until they are cleaned and cooked. We have been acculturated to the social patterns of carnism—they are not natural. We don't like raw skin with hair or fur still attached to meat. We don't like scales on fish. We must have these items removed because we are not truly carnivores. We are herbivoric frugivores and we are altruistic. We are more aligned to eat fruit and vegetables than anything else, and that is the reason we are not attracted to raw flesh, sinew, and blood; we are not designed by nature to eat it.

Anatomically, physiologically, biologically, and psychologically, we are not carnivores and thus not attracted to the smell, look, and taste of raw blood. If we were carnivores, we would all revel in the eating of raw skin, raw flesh, and raw fur—and not be repelled by it. We would not need or even want to cook our food, as its natural, raw state would be most beautiful to us and the healthiest for our bodies. Jobs in slaughterhouses would be highly sought after and enviable, rather than undesirable, low paid, and vilified. It is a well-documented fact that slaughterhouse workers suffer greatly and that violent crime rates are higher in the communities where they live. To kill thousands of animals each day and night, to put a bolt gun to their heads, slit their throats, and cut them into small pieces takes a toll on workers. Working in these conditions, one must disassociate from normal human feelings of empathy and compassion for hours, days, and years on end. Slaughterhouse workers learn to disassociate themselves from the violence they cause, but in the end they suffer from PTSD, anxiety, drug and alcohol abuse, and domestic violence.

Not coincidentally, these are similar in many ways to military communities with their well-documented higher rates of domestic abuse. When we as normally empathetic beings are traumatized day in and day out, we create coping mechanisms; however, each and every piece of meat has violence and emotional trauma attached to it, whose outcome is not only visited upon the slaughtered animals at work but upon loved ones and the community at large. Child abuse, property crimes, and arrest rates for violent crimes such as rape are 166% higher in communities where a slaughterhouse exists. As Amy Fitzgerald, Assistant Professor, University of Windsor, Ontario, Canada, has documented, an average slaughterhouse, with 175 workers, can predict an increase in arrests and reports of rape in the community where it exists. Fitzgerald's work is supported by other studies which show a relationship between higher rape statistics and the presence of slaughterhouses in a community. [73] [74] [75] [76] [77] [78] Killing others is not our natural state, but rather a learned state with very negative consequences. We are not equipped anatomically, physiologically, biologically, or psychologically to kill others without losing our humanity.

Some may point out instances where survival was obtained by the eating of raw fish and meat; for instance, someone stranded at sea. But the question discussed here is not whether we can survive on raw animal flesh, because the answer to that question is simply yes. Rather the question being discussed is if eating the bodies of animals in their raw state is our most natural and therefore healthiest food. The answer to this question is unequivocally, no. It is not the healthiest, nor is it the most natural. The foods that influenced the building of our bodies from millions of years of evolution are those most suited to us. Our anatomical, physiological, biological, and psychological heritage is a legacy which has evolved from eating fruits and vegetables. This is an altruistic and compassionate heritage, and as such it forms the foundation for the possibility of the fully awakened state.

The truth is most of us do not want to kill animals and could stop eating meat if we had to do so. Eating meat is not in line with our true altruistic and compassionate nature. Humans are kind creatures who wish to help others, not harm them. We have far more of a sharing, caring, and helping nature than we do a harming nature, despite what we see in the media. We even play word games, mentally, in trying to hide the fact we are eating animals by giving the body parts different names, like beef (not cow), pork (not pig), veal (not baby calf), steak (not steer) and burger, to make the eating of animals more tolerable.

The Bussineau Carnivore Test

If we were carnivores, our natural appetite would be raw flesh, either freshly killed or even ripe and rotting for a couple days. Here is the test:

> The next time you are hungry, in a motor vehicle, and you pass by a recently dead animal in the road, do a meditative check of your mental and physical state. Are your saliva glands activated? Are you attracted to the dead body of the squirrel, raccoon, deer, dog, cat, or whatever animal it is? If you are a true carnivore, and have not just eaten, your juices are flowing, you are enticed and hungry when you look at the roadkill.

Not sure? Stop your vehicle. Get out and walk over to the dead body. Stoop down and get on your knees and smell the body just as all carnivores do. Does it smell good?

Pick up the carcass and rip it open. Eat it raw, just as you found it. Tear out its guts and eat those, too. If you can do all these things, enjoy them, and not become deathly ill from eating this dead animal (as it snakes through your intestines for the next 12 to 24 hours) you, my friend, are a true carnivore.

However, if you are like me and roadkill saddens you, slightly disgusts you, and is not appetizing in its raw form, then you are not a carnivore. There are many roadkill jokes and stories. Freshly killed deer are harvested by hunters in the state of Michigan all the time. In such cases they are eaten not by carnivores, but rather by humans who must cut, clean, process, and cook the deer. Humans are not carnivores.

The Four Noble Truths and Health?

Health is the greatest gift, contentment the
greatest wealth, faithfulness the best relationship.
The Buddha

To know compassion, you must first have it for
yourself. If you don't know how to help yourself,
you cannot help others.
Gelek Rimpoche

It is clear from the work of Campbell, Fuhrman, Barnard, Greger, Kahn, Klapper, Esselstyn, and many others that a plant-based diet is the one diet best suited for human beings to live as free of chronic disease as possible. These diseases have been shown by scientific study to plague populations who eat the SAD diet heavy in meat, fish, dairy, eggs, and fat. If we are to follow the advice of the Buddha, Atisha, Je Tsongkhapa, Pabonka Rinpoche, and the myriad other learned Buddhist masters who have taught the Lam Rim stages, we should probably meditate and think deeply on this. Taking advantage of this precious human life is an essential point on the path. If this life is precious, it follows we should take care of this body. This body is easily lost through heart disease, various cancers, and diabetes, many of which are implicated by diet. We should be empowered by scientific knowledge, awareness, and understanding to take positive action to safeguard our body to serve us as best it can until death, without wheel chairs, bags full of pills, and without a potentially preventable, suspendable, or reversible disease.

In a defensive posturing one may feel and state that this body is impermanent. It's just a "rented apartment," as many teachers will tell us. So what's the use, we may ask. The use is there is a connection between the body, mind, and spirit, and until we reach our spiritual goals we need to use our body as a vehicle to get there. It's our way to get there, our only way. However, when the body is in pain it is difficult to do anything, let alone practice yoga and meditate. When the body cannot sit on a cushion or a chair, or even lie down without painful consequence due to bad health, how will that help us on our path? Indeed the reason we should care for our body is because it is so fragile and impermanent. It means we should not trash it. When we learn something new to help it, we should implement the new discovery. And this doesn't necessarily mean we should become attached to our body or an ideology, but that we should apply pliancy as there is a middle path between causing our body disease and becoming attached to it.

Negligence of our body was not given to us as direction by the Buddha. Thus is it right to continue to harm our body when science shows we do not need animal foods for health? Indeed, these foods are associated with disease, so is it right to continue to consume food that harms the body? Is it following spiritual advice to deny science? Is it following the middle path to cause harm to our coronary arteries and endothelium functions by eating a high-fat diet? Is it pursuing the middle path to cause diabetes, cancers, strokes, and other ailments by continuing to be attached to our diets?

Buddhism is all about realizing our ignorance and making positive change. So, if we believe in science, the scientific method, peer-reviewed research, and Buddhist teachings, we should be concerned enough to take care of ourselves and others in our circle, and to expand this sphere of compassion outward by eating foods that produce health and not chronic illness. One fundamental Buddhist teaching is love for all sentient beings. This love starts with love for our own self, since without love for myself, how can we even begin to love others?

Can I say I love for myself and yet we continue down the path causing a chronic disease that could be suspended or reversed with a change in diet? If we don't love ourselves enough to take care of our precious human body, do we really value our life and even the lives of others?

The first teaching of the Buddha was the Four Noble Truths. The Four Noble Truths can be looked at from a variety of viewpoints. One is that they are about health, a healthy, realistic outlook on our personal lives (body, mind and spirit). They are grounded in an honest assessment of our state of being. Being healthy and having an honest assessment is not about cheating death. We can't do that. We are all impermanent and will die. The Four Noble Truths of health is about getting to the root of our problem until it is our time to depart. This is about living our lives in relative health, without expensive procedures and medications that do nothing but treat symptoms.

The Buddha is compared to a doctor in many teachings in that he taught how to get to the root of our problems. Verse 24 from Shantideva's book, *Guide to the Bodhisattva's Way of Life* states:

> Yet the Supreme Physician does not employ
> Common medical treatment such as these,

With an extremely gentle technique
He remedies all the greatest ills.[79]

This verse tells us the supreme physician, Buddha, does not use violent methods to treat, but gentle, compassionate ones. In modern terms this can mean that instead of taking statin drugs for high cholesterol and triglycerides while continuing to eat meat, fish, dairy and eggs, we switch to an earth-friendly, sustainable WFPB diet. It can mean instead of opting for having our chest opened up for heart surgery, we cure with gentle means our own heart disease by eating an earth-friendly, sustainable WFPB diet. It points toward the alternative to shooting ourselves full of insulin, getting kidney disease, and continuing to eat meat, fish, dairy, and eggs and choosing to heal ourselves by eating plants. Certainly, it is gentler to eat WFPB diet rather than undergo violent chemotherapy, stents, bypasses, amputations, drugs with lethal side effects, and other brutal procedures. Certainly it is more compassionate to eat our way to health, when possible, rather than submit to common medical procedures and drugs which tend to treat nothing but symptoms related to eating animals and their secretions.

Buddhism empowers us to get to the source of own problems and do so with gentle, compassionate techniques. The Buddha has been described as a teacher, a guide, and a servant, in addition to a doctor who prescribes the right treatment which we are empowered to implement or act upon. We are responsible for our own activities. Empowerment and responsibility gives us the control and the obligation to change our habitual patterns. The Four Noble Truths inform us how to go about doing this. They are basic analytical tools and techniques. These four truths can and do relate to not only mental, emotional, and spiritual freedom, but also the liberty to choose health over illness through application of an ethical, healthy WFPB diet.

1) The First Noble Truth: The Truth of Suffering

The First Noble Truth is the truth of suffering. From a Buddhist vegan's vantage, this can look like the following:

More than one-third (36.5%) of U.S. adults are obese.[80] This affects all aspects of health and is a forerunner of disease. Self-esteem can be injured, mobility is compromised, energy levels are reduced, and disorders such as heart disease, certain cancers, and diabetes are promoted. This is suffering.

Each year, 610,000 men and women die from heart attacks in the U.S.[81] The pain and suffering this causes is untold. The people who die do so earlier than they would have on a WFPB diet. Their families are robbed of their presence. They, in many cases, lived lives which were very fearful, perhaps took a lot of pills and underwent procedures for their condition. All these pills had their side effects. Pills are not healthy, unless absolutely needed, as they cause sickly conditions, and those who are being treated live with those sickly conditions. The procedures are expensive, painful, and hard to recover from; they cause enormous distress and impairment. This is suffering.

Each year approximately 595,000 people die of cancer in the U.S.[82] It has been shown there is a correlation between cancer and animal protein through the China Study, the largest epidemiological study ever performed. Cancer is a disease that causes a lot of suffering, in many instances taking months and years to end in death. It takes its toll on all the afflicted's loved ones. The treatment of chemotherapy is suffering, because we take poison to kill the cancer and the poison makes us suffer and kills us, too. We struggle to have good days. Bad days are horrendous bouts of nausea and pain. This is suffering.

Nearly 30 million, or 9.3%, of the U.S. population, have diabetes.[83] Type 2 diabetes, the most prevalent type, is a disease of diet. There are many years of suffering from this disease. Diabetes, and the drugs used to treat diabetes, spawn many other ailments, such as loss of limbs, sight, and mobility. Insulin takes its toll, too, whether by pill or injection. All the organs of the body deteriorate, constructing a gateway to myriad other disease conditions. This is suffering.

2) The Second Noble Truth: The Cause of Suffering

The root cause of suffering is ignorance. What we eat is killing us and we are generally ill-informed or unconscious of this fact.

In societies where the average cholesterol level is 150 mg/dL or lower, heart disease does not exist. When we eat foods that contain cholesterol and saturated fat, we get arteriosclerosis, heart disease. When we eat a high-fat, animal-protein diet, we produce an environment in our bodies which cancer cells enjoy and in which they can multiply. When we eat a diet high in fat from animal products, we create the cause for diabetes, as our cells can no longer let insulin inside and it just runs through our bloodstream without anywhere to go. We believe we are eating a healthy diet, a diet high in protein, a diet prescribed by the Food and Drug Administration, a diet following the food pyramid, a diet our families ate, and a diet we love. However, we are ignorant of the fact we are killing ourselves with each and every bite of meat, fish, dairy, and eggs. This is the cause of suffering.

3) The Third Noble Truth: There Is a Way Out – Nirvana

Nirvana is peace and so is a WFPB diet. Your body will be at more peace and healthier when eating just vegetables, fruits, and grains. Vegan nirvana is health when based on a whole-foods plant-based diet. Vegan nirvana is peace when based on a WFPB diet. Vegan nirvana is an absence of suffering caused by foods of animal origin. There is a way out of many health problems we take for granted and blame on genetics. We can go vegan and eat a WFPB diet.

4) The Fourth Noble Truth: The Path (to eliminating suffering)

The Buddha taught there is a path to get out of samsara and wake up to our ignorance. In the Tibetan Gelug tradition, this is the Lam Rim. In other traditions it follows the Eight-Fold Path. From a health perspective, here is what the eight-fold path looks like:

- Right view or understanding. This is based on seeing that our bodies are naturally evolved to eat plants. We can eat animal products and survive, but they cause disease. Right view is the foundation of a healthy mind and body, and it allows us to transform ourselves. We seek out the best science available, read the information, and have dialogue with others to understand the information. Right view is cultivated by interaction with informed individuals, organizations, and scientific data. They are essentially our health sangha.

- Right thought or attitude relates to having an informed mind, which knows eating animals will cause us disease and suffering, and we know we are free to change our minds and practice eating a WFPB diet. Others eat a WFPB diet, and thus I know that I can. Therefore, I can be liberated from my past practice. Once we have the information and understanding, we commit with the right attitude and thought patterns.

- Right speech is the ability to speak clearly and truthfully about the path to better health. Once we learn the truth about eating animal-based foods and their relationship to disease states, we learn to speak honestly to ourselves internally and to others so they can be helped.

- Right action means that we will follow the WFPB diet. We will clean out our pantries, take a 30-day pledge, and act in ways leading to eating plants and only plants. Once we have the information, understanding, and commitment we take action. We act ethically toward what we have just learned for our own health and that of our family, community, and world.

- Right livelihood means we learn to cook healthy, WFPB dishes. We enthusiastically retrain ourselves and learn to veganize our favorite foods. In doing so, we stop exploiting our health and well-being and learn to live in a more ideal state.

- Right effort means we give it our all. Going at something half-heartedly will give us poor results. We learn to become creative in our efforts and are full of energy and vitality. We become diligent, and our diligence pays off in life-transforming action in which we become more whole, creating a new habit pattern based on choice rather than blind precedents taught by culture, media, and consumerism.

- Right mindfulness means that we now become acutely aware of things that try to change us back to eating in an unhealthy way. We guard our newfound freedom and health through an awareness of our own feelings and thoughts, as well as other people's feelings and thoughts which may impinge upon us. When a craving comes up for an animal product, we simply choose to look at it and pause. Mindfully we hesitate and do analytical meditation and concentrated meditation. Our non-reaction, analysis, and concentration is the cause for the craving to evaporate.

- We meditate formally or informally. Meditation
  means we spend time concentrating and becoming
  aware at a deeper level how this change is pervading
  our entire being. Meditation on the change to a WFPB
  diet can take a few seconds or minutes once we
  become accustomed to it. It's just a simple function of
  checking in on a daily basis, either on a cushion, at the
  table, or in line at the grocery store. No need to be
  cross-legged in the form of a yogi or Buddha. Just be
  present. Concentrate and absorb yourself on the path
  of becoming a WFPB vegan and rejoice in the small
  but important enlightenment this change can bring
  about in your health, as well as your family's health,
  community, and world.

Prevent, Suspend, and Cure

At lectures Dr.Campbell quite often uses the following slide in his PowerPoint deck. I first saw this at a lecture of his in 2014 and he kindly gave permission to reprint it here. Extremely empowering, it is based on solid, peer-reviewed science. Now that we have this evidence, we can chose positivity over negativity or better health over poorer health. The choice, path, and responsibility are ours. We can choose reactivity, to react like we always have been taught by cultural habit and taste unmindfully, or we can choose to be mindful, ethical, and healthier. The choice is ours.

"Whole Food, Plant-Based Diet Prevents, Suspends and/or Cures All (peer-reviewed research findings)[84]

- *Cancers*
- *Cardiovascular Diseases*
- *Multiple Sclerosis*
- *Kidney Stones*
- *Osteoporosis*
- *Diabetes (1 and 2)*
- *Rheumatoid Arthritis*
- *Obesity*
- *Erectile Dysfunction**
- *Macular Degeneration*
- *Hypertension*
- *Acne*
- *Migraine*
- *Lupus*

- *Depression*
- *Alzheimer's Disease*
- *Cognitive Dysfunction*
- *Pain**

  * Anecdotal"

The Planet

Did You Say You Care for the Environment?

The earth I tread on is not a dead inert mass. It is a body—has a spirit—is organic—and fluid to the influence of its spirit—and to whatever particle of the spirit is in me.
Henry David Thoreau[85]

As a family, we have for many years owned fuel-efficient vehicles. Currently we own a Volt and it gets better than 120 mpg. We use canvas bags at the grocery, and when we forget to put them back in the vehicle we ask for recyclable paper bags. We have two large bins provided by the garbage company for recycling, but that isn't enough for our household and so we went out and purchased an additional container. We try to properly recycle everything we can, so we save up our electronics and hazardous materials for our township's biannual recycling collection. We try to limit water consumption and energy usage. All the lights in our home are now LED. We keep the heat low in the winter months and add an extra layer of clothing. We have numerous stainless steel bottles, for filling and taking with us, rather than use plastic water bottles. On a personal level, isn't that enough to help the planet heal and combat climate change? Isn't it enough when in conjunction with recycling we drive a very fuel-efficient hybrid or electric car or 40-plus-mpg vehicle? No, it's not. We can all do better.

What I was surprised to learn was that the single largest action taken by my family and I to combat climate change, to help the earth and our environment, was to become vegan. Being vegan outstrips all these actions combined.

Livestock Versus All Transportation

According to the United Nations Food and Agriculture Organization report in 2006, "the livestock sector generates more greenhouse gas emissions as measured in CO_2 equivalent... than transport. It is also a major source of land and water degradation."[86] Let me paraphrase: The agricultural livestock sector—beef and dairy—when summed up for grazing, factory farming, slaughter and transport creates more CO_2 equivalent gas than all the cars, trucks, planes, jets, ships, boats, trains, motorcycles, and mopeds on the planet combined. Transport accounts for 13% and livestock for 18%. This same report goes on to say, "Livestock now uses 30% of the earth's entire land surface, mostly permanent pasture but also including 33% of the global arable land used to producing feed for livestock... As forests are cleared to create new pastures, it is a major driver of deforestation, especially in Latin America where, for example, some 70% of former forests in the Amazon have been turned over to grazing."[87]

The report furthermore states, "The livestock business is among the most damaging sectors to the earth's increasingly scarce water resources, contributing among other things to water pollution, eutrophication and the degeneration of coral reefs. The major polluting agents are animal wastes, antibiotics and hormones, chemicals from tanneries, fertilizers, and the pesticides used to spray feed crops. "[88] However, since 2006 the situation has declined, today 45% of earth's non-ice-covered surface is used for livestock.[89]

All in all, this is a pretty sobering picture that had gone unnoticed by me until my transition to a plant-based diet. Additionally, subsequent research shows this data does not factor in what we take from the oceans, just land-based livestock. What we choose to eat affects the environment tremendously. Since the inception of that report, the damage has continued and perhaps worsened as our demand and appetite for even more animal flesh has grown globally since 2006. In a new report from the United Nations entitled, "Climate Change 2014: Impacts, Adaptation, and Vulnerability" data is showing that climate change is affecting agriculture, human health, ecosystems, water supplies and people's livelihoods.[90]

In 2014 National Geographic noted[91] we will need to double the quantity of crops we grow by 2050 to feed the world's population, since the demand for a Standard American Diet heavy in meat, fish, eggs, and dairy is increasing due to economic affluence. The corollary to this is, of course, we need to grow more corn and soy to feed directly to animals, which would mean 90% of the earth's surface would need to be devoted to livestock. This would also double the carbon dioxide, nitrous oxide, and methane emissions too. Last time I checked we didn't have another earth, just this one, so we had better figure this out and fast.

According to a study done by Chalmers University of Technology, the cutting of greenhouse gas emission from the cars, trucks, trains, and ships we use for transportation will not be enough on its own to ensure global temperatures rise no more than 2 degrees Celsius.[92] We need to do more than drive a Prius. They have demonstrated it is necessary to cut the emission from agriculture if we are going to make an impact on global warming. Dr. Fredrik Hedenus, the lead scientist of the study, believes they have established a key component to reduction of agricultural climate change pollution is decreased consumption of meat and dairy. This is also borne out in similar fashion by experts, like Ilmi Granoff from the Overseas Development Institute, who suggests that reducing emissions from cars and coal is an insignificant solution, informing us to: "Forget coal, forget cars," rather reduce meat consumption.[93]

~~56 Billion Land Animals 59 Billion Land Animals~~ 70 Billion Land Animals

There are 7 billion humans on the earth, but there are billions more animals in factory farms. Animals we consider food. The strike-through font in the subhead is intentional. When I started writing this manuscript in 2014, the generally agreed upon number of land animals we breed, confine, grow, and slaughter was between 56 and 59 billion. That number has, however, increased to 70 billion.[94] [95] [96] These 70 billion animals create a lot of waste and use a lot of resources—70 billion animals annually cut up into little pieces and put into Styrofoam packages and refrigerated 24/7 use a lot of oil, gas, and electricity. Those billions upon billions of body parts are all delivered to groceries around the globe. Even the middle-of-the-road, generally conservative, *Reader's Digest* tells us to change what is on our plates if we want to change the world, informing us that almost 20% of pollution made by humans comes from agribusiness for the production of meat.[97] They echo the UN by advising us that factory farming contributes more to greenhouse effect than transportation and that it takes 40 calories of fossil fuel to create 1 calorie of beef from a feedlot. This is opposed to 2.2 calories of fossil fuel it takes to create 1 calorie of plant protein. Meat-eaters who call themselves environmentalists should take note. As PETA recently pointed out, the production of just two strips of bacon generates three times the greenhouse gases that operating a Prius for 1 mile does.[98] So if you consider yourself an environmentalist you should consider these facts carefully.

Based on this knowledge, American novelist and author of *Eating Animals*, Jonathan Safran Foer articulates that someone who regularly eats factory-farmed meat cannot call themselves environmentalist without divorcing themselves from the meaning of the word, pointing out, "The most current data even quantifies the role of diet: Omnivores contribute seven times the volume of greenhouse gases that vegans do."[99]

Sea Shepherd Conservation Society's Paul Watson believes everyone needs an education on this subject and laments the fact that the "biggest inconvenient truth" in Al Gore's movie of the same title is that it never mentions the role of animal agriculture in the climate change gas emissions. Not once. Steak-eating contributes more to global warming than driving a car. To this point he states, "A vegan driving a Hummer contributes less than a meat-eater riding a bicycle."[100] Cars, trucks, ships, and trains may produce carbon dioxide, but meat is responsible for methane and nitrous oxide production, which is respectively 86 and 296 times more injurious to earth's atmosphere than carbon dioxide.

Carbon Dioxide, Methane, and Nitrous Oxide

Greenhouse gas comes in three primary varieties: carbon dioxide , methane , and nitrous oxide . Each gas has different properties, but all have the ability to hold warmth and act as a blanket, trapping heat in our atmosphere. Carbon dioxide enters the atmosphere through burning fossil fuels (coal, natural gas, and oil), solid waste, trees, and wood products. Methane is emitted during the production and transport of coal, natural gas, oil, livestock, and other agricultural processes. It is also emitted by the decay of organic waste in municipal solid waste landfills and especially the millions of gallons of waste in factory farm open-air lagoons hidden from the public eye. Nitrous oxide is emitted during agricultural and industrial activities, as well as during combustion of fossil fuels and solid waste.[101]

Some gases are more effective than others at making the planet warmer and "thickening the Earth's blanket." To account for these differences, each gas has a Global Warming Potential (GWP), reflecting how long it remains in the atmosphere, on average, and based on how strongly it absorbs energy. Gases with a higher GWP absorb more energy, per pound, than gases with a lower GWP, and thus contribute more to warming Earth.[102] The GWP for carbon dioxide is 1, methane is 86, and nitrous oxide is 296.

As a side note, you may see EPA quoted statistics utilizing a GWP for methane of 20 or 25; however, most concerned scientists are utilizing the more accurate GWP of 86, based on a 20-year peak rather than 100 years. Why? Simply put we don't have another 100 years to figure this out.[103 104105]

Empty Oceans by 2048

Commercial fishing kills more animals worldwide than any other business, using football field-size ships equipped with all types of technologies to locate and capture fish. They are furnished with large freezers and can stay at sea for very long periods of time. Estimates range from 1 trillion to 2.7 trillion sea creatures killed per year by the commercial fishing industry. Predatory fish, cod, sharks, halibut, grouper, tuna, swordfish, and marlin, have declined from their 1950s populations by 90% as of 2003.[106] Additionaly, this 90 percent decline in predatory fish has been witnessed in 39 coral reefs across the Caribbean by researchers at the University of North Carolina in a study published in the journal of Science Advances, 2017.[107] [108] The entire biomass of the world's oceans has been reduced by two-thirds since the 1970s.[109] This is due to a single cause: our love of eating seafood. Some estimates predict the entire collapse of the oceans systems for sustaining life by the year 2048.[110] [111]

Weapons of Mass Destruction

The ways we catch fish commercially include trawling, dredging, purse seine netting, longlining, and gillnetting. To find the fish many types of devices are used, including radar, echo sounders, and sonar. GPS and autopilot technologies interface with all the onboard electronics. Radar is used to spot bird flocks feeding over a school of fish, and with the click of a button GPS translates the way on a chart plotter, which provides latitude and longitude, distance, bearing and even which direction the flock is heading. Sonar gives a clear image of what's below once the ship has reached the destination.[112]

Bottom Trawling – Clear-Cutting Our Oceans

Bottom trawling is an extremely destructive method which irreversibly harms habitat for all sea life. Bottom trawling pulls enormous weighted nets across the seafloor, scooping everything in their route. This of course means targeted fish (the fish wishing to be captured) and else everything in its path, including coral reef habitats. While the target fish for bottom trawls are shrimp, cod, sole, and flounder, the problem is this unselective process results in up to 90% bycatch, other species that are then thrown overboard as garbage.[113] This is permanent damage and we are connected to this when we choose to eat fish.

How much trawling is done every year? University of Hawaii Zoology professor Dr. Les Watling states "Trawling is the most destructive of any actions that humans conduct in the ocean...Ten years ago, [1998] Elliot Norse and I calculated that each year, worldwide, bottom trawlers drag an area equivalent twice the lower 48 states." [114] Super trawlers are extreme example of this way of fishing with nets large enough to contain 13 jumbo jets, and while their target fish is sardines and smaller prey fish, they also catch seals, dolphins, sharks and turtles too. These animals are unable to escape and are discarded as bycatch.[115]

Purse Seining – Clan Carnage

The National Oceanic and Atmospheric Administration defines a purse seine as"a large wall of netting deployed around an entire area or school of fish. The seine has floats along the top line with a lead line threaded through rings along the bottom. Once a school of fish is located, a skiff encircles the school with the net. The lead line is then pulled in, 'pursing' the net closed on the bottom, preventing fish from escaping by swimming downward. The catch is harvested by either hauling the net aboard or bringing it alongside the vessel."

Purse seine nets catch entire communities of fish. Fish are so very sentient and have their own communities. This must be so stressful to have everyone you know captured and killed. This is like catching an entire town or city. Plus, the purse seine catches more than what is intended, including sea turtles and dolphins, and there are no regulations for minimizing bycatch. [116]

Longlining – Miles of Misery

Longline fishing is exactly how it sounds. Long lines with up to 12,000 baited hooks are let out for 30 to 80 miles, snagging and catching all types of sea life. While the target fish is tuna of all types, Bonita, and large pelagics, the unintended bycatch comes in the form of any life that comes into contact with the barbs and hooks including 160,000 birds, 300,000 sea turtles, and millions of sharks annually. Nineteen of the 22 species of Albatross are on the endangered with extinction due to longline fishing. While some new reports show that there are areas of the world where conservation efforts are making a modest impact and fewer birds are being killed, these efforts are not enough, as longlining is not regulated or enforced. But we all know a sure way to make a 100% reduction in sea bird deaths from longlining and stop the march of Albatross to extinction—stop eating fish. [117] [118] [119] [120] [121] [122] [123]

Gillnetting – Walls of Suffering

Gillnetting uses a wall of netting with webbing large enough for the target fish to put their head into but not large enough to get their body through. This creates a terrible period of suffering for the fish that cannot escape who struggle, unable to breathe, until they die in the net. Nets are left in the water from a few hours to a few days. The suffering is immense. This suffering is met by not only the target fish but also from other mammals and fish who are unintended bycatch: whales, dolphins, turtles, sharks, sea lions, Harbor porpoise, and many species of fish. Included in the bycatch are endangered species such as sperm, humpback, and North Atlantic right whales, Pacific leatherback turtles, and Bluefin tuna. [124] [125] [126] [127] [128] [129] [130]

Sardines And Sea Lions – Slaughter of the Largest Habitat on Earth

The National Oceanic and Atmospheric Administration informs us that "pelagic fish can be categorized as coastal and oceanic fish, based on the depth of the water they inhabit. Coastal pelagic fish inhabit sunlit waters up to about 655 feet deep... Examples of species include forage fish such as anchovies, sardines, shad, and menhaden and the predatory fish that feed on them... The pelagic zone is the largest habitat on earth with a volume of 330 million cubic miles."[131]

Sardines and anchovies are pelagic fish. We have been catching them, eating them, and decimating their numbers by overfishing for many years. We know this. The complete collapse has been predicted for quite a few years. [132] But when baby sea lions wash ashore starving and dying, it breaks our hearts, and now for the third year in a row there is a complete moratorium on fishing for sardines in the Pacific Northwest from Alaska to Mexico. [133] [134] Will it be enough to save sardines, anchovies, sea lions, and other pelagic wildlife? We don't know. But we do know that continuing to eat sea life is not healthy for them, us, or the oceans.

Mixed Messages From Advocates

As an email list subscriber, but not a financial supporter of Oceana, I have often been sent heartbreaking photos of baby sea lions and their mothers who are both emaciated from lack of food. The request for donations to help these poor creatures is compassionate, heart-felt, and compelling until we dig a little deeper. When we look below the surface we find insincerity and duplicity.

Sardines and anchovies are one of the main food sources for sea lions. Mother sea lions are obligate carnivores, and without a steady supply of this high-quality food they do not get the proper nutrition to feed their pups, who then starve to death.[135] [136] [137] [138] When we look beyond the email requests we find that while Oceana (and the Monterey Bay Aquarium's Seafood Watch) say they want to help sea lions yet they also support the fishing industry. They have a guide to the fish we can eat sustainably and make "ocean-friendly choices." [139] This is a complete hypocrisy, akin to concept of humane slaughter. We cannot say on the one hand we care for oceans and then create a program that helps consumers and businesses make choices for a healthy ocean by killing ocean life. Sounds a lot like, *I love you therefore I will kill you and eat you,* an absolute absurdity.

And even though sardine fishing is banned, the Monterey Bay Aquarium's guide as of June 2017 still lists them as one of the "best choices" for consumers to eat. Best choice, according to their definition: "Buy first, they're well managed and caught or farmed responsibly."[140] How can a population of fish be well managed or responsibly caught in light of a full 3-year moratorium? This sounds like they are advocating for extinction.

Coral Reefs – If This Then That

Coral reefs are important. They support life for myriad small creatures which form a web of connectivity to the entire oceanic ecosystem. It is estimated that 25% of all ocean life is supported in some manner by coral reefs, with 4,000 species of fish dependent upon them during their lifecycle.[141] They are severely impacted by a number of human activities, such as the choice consume animal products, warming temperatures, and GHG emissions.

Climate change is affected by the food we choose to eat, as are coral reefs. The only way we can supply the immense amount of meat, fish, dairy, and eggs that the general public demands is through factory farming. When we eat foods from factory farms we choose to be part of an intensive cycle of massive crop growth, runoff, and

GHG emissions. We are, by choice, choosing to eat high on the carbon chain.

We know that ocean acidification is caused by GHG. Scientifically, we have been able to measure a 30% increase in ocean acidity over the industrial era, and we are predicted to have oceans as acidic as they were 20 million years ago—caused by our human activity. The earth's oceans will never be the same. Many creatures (mollusks, crustaceans, corals, coralline algae, and foramaniferans) will not be able to make shells they need for growth and survival, as their basic building blocks will be missing from ocean water due to acidification. This will have a major impact on all ocean life, especially on food webs. When acidification decreases the number of small animals like clams, oysters, and sea urchins, the larger animals that feed on them will run out of food, and so on. [142] [143] [144] [145] Indeed, coral reefs have been called "cradles of evolution," and acidification is inhibiting coral from being able to calcify, and bleaching death is occurring around the world. The Great Barrier Reef, so large it can be seen from space, is believed by many scientists to be in a terminal bleaching state due to human activity. [146] [147] [148] [149] [150]

Reefs around the world have been and continue to be destroyed by our fishing techniques, especially trawling. The single most important thing we can personally do for the world's oceans is to stop eating fish. The second most important thing we can do is take animal products off our plates. If we do this, we allow our oceans to repopulate and reduce the amount of GHG we personally contribute to ocean acidification. Tropical coral reefs, cold-water deep sea corals, coastal and open-ocean planktonic ecosystems need our help. [151] [152] [153] [154] [155] [156]

Saying we care for the oceans and continuing to eat seafood is falsehood, as is continued eating of any animal products. All these activities are connected in the web of life or death. We choose. We vote in favor of life or death on earth with every meal.

Fresh Water

Nitrogen Pollution of Fresh Water

Factory farming, with the increased concentration of animals and the corresponding concentration of manure production, accounts for much of the nitrogen pollution of our waterways. The milk you drink and the yogurt you eat may be one of the main culprits of nitrogen pollution. According to the EPA, dairy cows produce more manure than beef cattle. Holstein cows, which dominate the U.S. dairy industry, produce almost twice as much manure as Jersey cows, which are also used in dairy. The USDA estimates that 200 cows on a milk farm produce as much nitrogen as the sewage from a community of 5,000 to 10,000 people. The biggest U.S. dairies now have 15,000 cows, equating to the same nitrogen production as a city of 375,000 to 750,000 people. In California, 100,000 square miles of polluted groundwater have been identified and attributed to nitrogen pollution from agriculture, which includes cows. California is a large dairy production state; in fact it's now the largest, with 1.8 million dairy cows to Wisconsin's 1.3 million.[157]

From Wisconsin to California we've seen multiple stories of runoffs from manure spills that threaten aquifers and generate lawsuits from residents whose water becomes unsafe. Clean Wisconsin staff attorney Elizabeth Wheeler believes the state has a nitrate problem.[158][159][160] Some reports claim that agriculture waste is the number one form of well-water pollutants in the U.S., with over 4 million Americans exposed to perilously high nitrate concentrations in their drinking water, all due to factory farming waste.[161] So what's wrong with a little extra nitrate? Nitrates are detrimental to human and animal health and have been shown to be related to thyroid problems, "blue baby" syndrome, and some cancers, and is associated with respiratory and reproductive disorders.[162] Environmentally, nitrate runoff causes dead zones and red tides, which kill aquatic life.

Lagoons

Lagoon. The word conjures up blue-green crystal clear water, with sweet breezes in the trees, and suntan lotion. But when we use this term in farming, we generally mean a manure lagoon used to capture and store feces, urine, and other waste. Factory farms produce an estimated 500 million tons of manure each year, more than three times the amount our human population produces. [163] [164] The lagoons on these farms are open-air pits, the largest holding between 20 and 40 million gallons of waste water.[165] These millions of gallons of urine and feces can rupture, break, and overflow during inclement weather, causing devastating environmental damage. When they leak, it is a worse situation than if raw municipal sewage leaked, since factory farmed manure is 160 times more toxic.[166] The billions of animals on industrial farms create tremendous amounts of manure which, unlike human feces and urine, is untreated. When an overflow occurs, waterways become polluted with harmful bacteria and antibiotic residues. We wouldn't think of not treating human waste, but we turn a blind eye to our complicit action when it comes to eating meat.

The pollution produced by these lagoons of waste threatens public health and our water, as not only are nitrate levels in our water supply increased but animal waste filters in disease-causing pathogens such as salmonella, E. coli, cryptosporidium, and fecal coliform. These organisms can be 10 to 100 times more concentrated in animal waste than in human waste, with more than 40 diseases that can be transferred to humans. In just one case manure from dairy cows is suspected to have contributed to the death of 100 people in Milwaukee's drinking water in 1993 through cryptosporidium contamination. Possible sources identified included cattle runoff into two rivers that flow into the Milwaukee harbor, slaughterhouses, and human sewage. [167]

Pig farms have large manure pits that emit hydrogen sulfide, which can be poisonous. While the average side effect for exposure to this gas are flu-like symptoms, high concentrations can lead to brain impairment. One of the most infamous events related to lagoon pollution occurred in 1995 when an 8-acre hog-waste lagoon in North Carolina spilled over and 25 million gallons of manure leaked into the New River, killing 10 million fish and closing 360,000 acres of coastal wetlands to shell fishing.[168] Similarly, in 2011, an Illinois hog farm spilled 200,000 gallons of manure, killing more than 110,000 fish.

When Hurricane Floyd hit North Carolina in 1999, 47 lagoons were completely flooded and five burst. The runoff from lagoons can create dead zones in oceans. A dead zone occurs when nutrients from agriculture and factory farm lagoons cause algae to rapidly grow, using up all the oxygen, which then kills off aquatic life. Additionally, ammonia freed during waste removal can be carried more than 300 miles through the air before being dumped into the water, where it can cause algae bloom and subsequent fish kill.[169] The choice to eat meat is tied to dead zones, explored in the next section.

Dead Zones – The Result of our Love for Flesh Food

Sentient life needs oxygen to live. Watching one's breath is one of the first meditations taught. Without breath there is no life. Without breath for a few minutes we die. We are that close to death. This is the same for animals who live in our oceans; without oxygen there is no life for them. Dead zones are areas in our oceans that lack the oxygen to support sea life normally found there. Dead zones can occur naturally. However, they are mostly owing to runoff from agriculture, manure lagoons, golf courses, suburban lawns, and sewage. The runoff carries with it so-called "nutrients" high in nitrogen and phosphorus (along with many other substances).[170] Plants thrive on these nutrients, and as these leach into streams, rivers, and underground water supplies, they eventually end up in the ocean and in our coastal waters. These coastal waters are teeming with life, whereas the open ocean has much less life.[171] When these excess nutrients end up in the ocean, the phytoplankton love it. They over multiply like crazy creating an algae bloom and then die, falling to the ocean floor. When they fall to the ocean floor, microbes consume the dead phytoplankton/algae[172] and, in the process, use up almost all of the oxygen, leaving the area depleted and unable to sustain life. This condition is known as hypoxia, the absence of enough oxygen in the bottommost waters for fish and other marine life to flourish.

In the 1960s there were only 49 dead (hypoxic) zones around the world. In 2003 the number had reached 146. In 2008 the number escalated to 400, and then exploded to 530 hypoxic zones in 2013, encompassing 95,000 square miles. That's 95,000 square miles of coastal water, the areas most abundant with marine life. It's like making our cities toxic and sparing the rural areas. These dead zones are located all around the planet and are linked to our unsustainable usage of chemical-based fertilizers. These dead zones are tied to our love for meat, dairy, and eggs, since much of the plants we grow are only grown as feed for animals we slaughter, milk, and take eggs from. There are dead zones off the coastlines of the United States, Europe, South America, China, Japan, New Zealand, Africa, Australia, and elsewhere. [173] [174] [175] [176]

One of the most infamous dead zones is in the Gulf of Mexico. This dead zone has doubled in size since the 1980s and is monitored closely. It was and has been the size of the state of Connecticut over the past several years (6,474 square miles). [177] [178]

This annual dead zone is caused by the runoff of farms into the streams and rivers that feed the Mississippi River. And if this wasn't bad enough, our continued search for energy sources to decrease our reliance on oil also affects this dead zone, since we now raise more corn, due to the Energy Independence and Security Act. Corn needs more nitrogen[179] than many other plants, and growing more corn to use for alternative fuels (like E-85) means there is more nitrogen on farm fields, which runs off into fields, streams, rivers, and then coastal ocean waters when it rains.

Few dead zones have ever been remediated, but we have the capability to reverse the trend. The Black

Sea, which had been considered one of the largest dead zones in the world, made a big comeback after the fall of the Soviet Union.[180] When the government fell, so did the usage of chemical fertilizers on the land that runs into the Black Sea. The elimination of excessive nutrient runoff allowed the sea to recover.

In addition, hurricanes have the ability to help dead zones recover when they agitate water by pure force. In essence, hurricanes mix oxygen-rich water from on top of the ocean with the oxygen-deficient water on the bottom. This effect was noticed in the Gulf of Mexico when Hurricane Katrina hit the Louisiana coast with winds of 130 mph. When Katrina was followed by Hurricane Rita a few months later, both storms ended the seasonal dead zone at the mouth of the Mississippi.[181]

A possible solution bandied about is the creation of a GMO (genetically modified organism) variety of plants that are more efficient in their uptake of nitrogen from the soil and thus need less nitrogen applied in order to grow.[182] This has not panned out yet and even if it did, it could cause even more damage from unknown and unintended consequences related to the lethal herbicides used to control weeds in GMO crops like Roundup (glyphosate), and other Agent Orange-type compounds.

Hoping for hurricanes is not the answer and neither is waiting for a scientific solution, which may cause other problems, when a simple, safe solution is right at our fingertips. We just need to begin eating plants directly, switch to organic, sustainable farms, and stop eating animals. If we all start eating a WFPB diet, the need for meat will be gone. As the market for meat goes away the need for all the agricultural food raised only for animals goes away. When we stop growing plants for 70 billion land animals and only grow it for 7 billion people the usage of fertilizer decreases. When the usage for fertilizer is reduced so are dead zones.

In the U.S., 85% of all the soybeans we grow, we feed directly to animals, not people.[183] 70% of all the corn we grow, we feed directly to animals, not to people.[184] We use at least 150 million acres of land to produce these crops. Conversely, if we consider the top ten vegetables consumed by humans in the U.S., we use less than 1 million acres to grow these crops.[185] [186] If we ate a vegan diet, we could for all intents and purposes leave over 100 million acres untouched. Just imagine 100 million acres with no added nitrogen, Roundup, pesticides, and ocean-killing potentiality. Problem solved in the Gulf of Mexico. The message is simple: Eat plants and eliminate dead zones and save sea life, human life, and the environment. The health of our oceans is inextricably tied to our cheese omelet in the morning, hamburger at lunch, and ribs at dinner. If you choose to eat meat, fish, dairy, and eggs, you are making a choice to kill ocean life.

Measurement is not Remediation

While it's a good thing for the oceans that the U.S. Congress reauthorized the Harmful Algal Bloom and Hypoxia Research and Control Act in 2014, which allows us to monitor, measure, and analyze dead zones, it does nothing in and of itself to help us bring back health to our oceans and coastlines.[187] Measurement does not equate to improvement. Neither does the Texas A&M project to build underwater gliders to measure dead zone attributes. Texas A&M (and all other universities) would be more helpful to students, future generations, and our oceans by providing education on how to change one's eating habits to a WFPB diet.[188] Similarly, our oceans would be better helped if Congress changed the food pyramid to one supporting a fully plant-based diet, a diet that supports the elimination of resource-intensive foods and factory farming that give us disease and cause us to create dead zones by the overgrowing of plants to feed animals rather than humans.

"Four Burgers, Please, and Hold the Showers"

California experienced one of the worst droughts ever recorded in 2014.The drought continued in 2015. One letter to the editor in a California newspaper typifies the attitude most of us bring to this issue—ignorance and pointing the finger outward. In the letter it was observed that many restaurants use oversize water glasses and that most people don't drink all the water provided. It was suggested by the well-meaning writer that smaller glasses should be used and only filled when requested. The writer acknowledged that it would take a lot more than this to solve the water crisis, but he offered this as a way to reduce usage at restaurants.[189] Never in this letter or in the general popular media is the true culprit of water scarcity acknowledged to be right on the menu in the form of animal foods.

In 2014, California Governor Jerry Brown's call for a 20% reduction in water usage fell on deaf ears as Californians used 1% more water than the previous year, despite the continued devastating drought. Beginning August 1, 2014 (but ending in 2016 despite continuing drought conditions) a ban on wasteful practice went into effect, where water users could be fined up to $500 per day for wasting water. Residents were no longer allowed to let water runoff from their outdoor sprinklers or hoses run down driveways and sidewalks. Even the use of drinking water in ornamental fountains that didn't recirculate were cause for one to face a stiff fine.[190] [191] To support and enforce this effort, additional officers had been hired to patrol the streets and look for the wasters. This is another example of pointing the finger out rather than looking at the true factors which cause water shortages—our food choices. In 2016, due to wetter than normal weather, the ban was lifted for urban areas despite the fact that three-fourths of the state is still under drought conditions.[192] [193]

Whenever I travel, I hang the towel on the hook, per the sign in the hotel stating if ends up on the floor it means you're done with it and if it's hung up it means you're going to use it again. These little signs are in every bathroom, in every chain it seems, and state how the management wants to reduce usage and help the environment by doing less laundry. I am sure you have seen the signage. Invariably, the towel I hung up in the morning (indicating reuse) is gone and replaced with a clean towel (ignoring their policy) when I return to the room. The only time they follow their policy is when I complain, and then I run the risk of getting someone in trouble. Are hotels really serious, I wonder, or is it simply for show?

Let's examine what you and I could do with taking fewer or shorter showers.

By most accounts it takes 25 to 50 gallons of water to take the average 8-minute shower.[194] The average shower head pumps out 5 gallons per minute whereas a "green" shower head pumps about 2.5 gallons per minute, depending on whether you use the standard 5-gpm shower head or a "green" model..[195] If you are the average person, you use between 20 and 40 gallons of water per shower. At 30 gallons per shower, the average person uses 7,800 gallons per year showering 5 days per week.

So to save water, what are we supposed to do, take fewer showers? Drink less water at restaurants? Stop watering the lawn? Stop washing cars? Use towels more than once? Yes, but how about also cutting down your meat consumption? Of course this is rarely mentioned or suggested unless you are a vegan or vegetarian. What about the alternative method of cutting meat consumption to reduce water usage. If you go vegan one day per month—just skip the two eggs for breakfast, the ¼-pound cheeseburger for lunch, the small daily glass of milk, and the 4-ounce chicken breast, and instead have a veggie burger, 1 cup of beans, a 4 ounce salad, and almond milk, you would save 500 gallons of water. If you went vegan one day per week, you could save more water than three people showering for an entire year.

What if you went completely vegan? The water savings are phenomenal. Approximately 86% of all the fresh water used in the world goes toward growing food.[196] Not for showering. Not for lawns, washing cars or drinking water at restaurants. Growing food for 7 billion people uses 86% of the fresh water. As demonstrated, changing your diet can have a big effect on your personal water usage, your water footprint. When we measure the usage of water over the entire supply chain, we find that water used to produce animal foods has the highest usage, with beef using the most of this precious resource.

In 2001, author of The Food Revolution, John Robbins informed us of that the "Water required to produce 1 pound of California foods, [was]according to Soil and Water specialists, University of California Agricultural Extension, working with livestock farm advisors:

- 1 pound of lettuce: 23 gallons
- 1 pound of tomatoes: 23 gallons
- 1 pound of potatoes: 24 gallons
- 1 pound of wheat: 25 gallons
- 1 pound of carrots: 33 gallons
- 1 pound of apples: 49 gallons
- 1 pound of chicken: 815 gallons
- 1 pound of pork: 1,630 gallons
- 1 pound of beef: 5,214 gallons. " [197] [198]

Many other studies have been performed, most with similar conclusions. In terms of beef, 5,163 gallons is the number based on a study by David Pimentel and others at Cornell University in 2004.[199] Gleick informs us it takes between 1,800 to 8,405 gallons of water to produce 1 pound of beef depending on where and how the beef is grown.[200] According to a 2011 global study by Mekonnen and Hoekstra, it takes 1,700 gallons of water to produce one pound of beef, 660 gallons to produce one pound of pork, and 264 gallons to produce one pound of chicken.[201] [202] National Geographic tells us it takes 1,800 gallons to produce 1 pound of beef.[203]

8,405 gallons, or 5,214, or 2,500, or 1,800 or 1,700 or whatever the true number is, it's a lot water to produce just four hamburgers. John Robbins message was clear, eat less meat if you want to save water and other resources. For the most part we have not heeded his message. We have not changed. For Californians, what should the message be? Take fewer showers or change your diet? What if there was a water tax on diet, or a rationing program where you could choose how to spend your annual allotment of fresh water? Would you order four burgers and skip showering for the entire year?

Should we be waiting until we run out of water to make a change? Or should we start today eating a healthy WFPB diet? The best solution, the most lasting solution, is not found in fewer showers but on our plates by eliminating animal-based foods.

Aquifers: Just Another Form of "Drill Baby Drill"

When we moved into our home in a semi-rural area outside Detroit, in 1980, it had a well. It was a 3-inch well dug at a depth of 125 feet and pulled enough water to suit the needs of our family for many years. Our neighbor to the right, in one of the original cottages, had a well that was at 50 feet. Her well ran dry and she had to have another one, a deeper one, dug to 145 feet. A few years later our well went dry, too, and we had to have another one dug. This time we installed a 6-inch well which was sunk at, you guessed it, 145 feet. Based on this data it would seem that in the past 30 years water tables have gone from 50 feet to 145 feet. I remember talking with the well driller and he confirmed, yes that is where the water level, generally, is in this area today. I didn't know anything about groundwater except it was there and we pulled it from the aquifer.

What's an aquifer? Aquifers are the saturated zone underground beneath the water table. They are huge depots of water in layers of rock, located in the voids or spaces between rocks. Wells can be dug into these types of layered water-bearing rocks and by use of a pump can transmit water to the surface. Aquifers have, as you might guess, a recharge rate based on rainfall. We pull water out and rainfall puts water back. But some aquifers recharge faster than others. Pumping more than the recharge rate draws an aquifer down and depletes it. [204]

This is what happened where I live. This is what is happening all over the world. Each well is the equivalent to a large straw going into the earth and sucking water out. Approximately 2 billion people in the world rely on groundwater as their primary source. So do farmers and agricultural corporations who irrigate their crops using wells. Sadly, GRACE satellites (NASA) have identified 40 major aquifers globally that are being depleted.[205] When these 40 aquifers are depleted they will have a huge impact on global food and water scarcity for everyone, not only the 2 billion people who depend on groundwater daily but also on our global food supply, since as much as 40% of the water utilized for irrigation is groundwater.

What is frightening it that aquifers are similar to fish in our oceans, climate change gas, and carnism: They are invisible. Due to their invisibility they become hard to comprehend and deal with, and have led to an attitude similar to that of the oil industry of "drill baby drill," because when one well goes dry we will just dig another.

The Ogallala, San Joaquin, and North China Basin

We don't grow food on just the amount of rain which falls from the sky. We did in the past but have not done so for many years, thanks to the invention of pumps. Today our production of grains, fruits, nuts, and vegetables depends upon the utilization of groundwater from aquifers. The Ogallala, San Joaquin, and North China Basin aquifers are three examples of groundwater sources used to grow food and provide drinking water to homes and communities. Unfortunately, these largest aquifers in the world are running dry because of overuse. In fact, their recharge rate is so low they basically cannot be replenished within our lifetime. All of these aquifers have three things in common: They are huge, are located in dry areas, and support millions of people and wildlife.

Some of the negative effects of groundwater depletion [are]:

- drying up of wells
- reduction of water in streams and lakes
- deterioration of water quality
- increased pumping costs
- land subsidence

> U.S. Geological Survey[206]

Drying Up of Wells

The Ogallala Aquifer in the U.S. runs partially under eight states from South Dakota to Texas, covering 175,000 square miles.[207] [208] It took between 1.8 and 3 million years to create this massive body of water, and anyone who knows the geography of the Great Plains knows it is a relatively dry locale. Why is it not renewable? The rock in this area is semipermeable and thus recharge rates are low. We pull 2.96 inches of water out of each year but only 0.86 inch gets restored, leaving a deficit of 2.1 inches. That may not seem like a lot, but over the past 60 years we have depleted the aquifer by 30%. This is exacerbated in a drought, as witnessed in Vega, Texas, which got 9 inches of rainfall in 2011, thus offering no replenishment to the Ogallala in that area—only extraction.[209]

We are not out of water yet, but we are getting there very rapidly. We are writing checks we cannot cash, as the Ogallala is expected to be out of water by 2060. Unfortunately for all of us, including farmers, there isn't a plan.[210] [211] [212] [213] [214]

In the U.S. there are no limitations for groundwater usage because if you own land, the water under your land belongs to you. You can do what you want with it. This short-sighted policy is another factor in the race to the bottom of the aquifer.[215] Additionally, we must remember that what is grown on much of these farms are crops used to feed animals, corn and soy. Approximately 94% of the water pumped from the Ogallala is for irrigation of crops. And looking at the U.S. in total, 80% of the water used is by agriculture.[216] [217] More than half of the crops are to feed animals, not people, and 14 trillion gallons are used to grow crops for livestock to ingest.[218] Thus cattle herds and the corn they live on are at the root of the exploitation and exhaustion of the Ogallala, and when wells run dry, farmers just drill another well.[219]

We act as if water is a fully renewable resource, but it is not. Aquifers take thousands of years to refresh and we know we are draining them faster than they can fill. While 70% of the world is covered by water, only 2.5%

is fresh water. Of that 2.5% only 1% can be accessed easily, and of that 1%, much of it is located in glaciers and ice, leaving only 0.007% available for 7.0 billion people to utilize.[220] The truth is that fresh water is scarce, and it is not fully renewable in the ways we consume it.

Riparian Ruin - Reduction of Water in Streams and Lakes

The area around lakes and streams that fosters life is called a riparian ecosystem. When a riparian ecosystem dies it denotes a triple loss: groundwater, native plants, and wild animals. Lowering of the water table by pumping out groundwater causes streams and lakes to dry up. When the water table decreases, native plants and trees also die because their roots cannot reach any water. The roots normally would be able to reach enough moisture underground to keep them alive during droughts and dry spells, but when the water is too low they cannot. The wildlife who depend on the plant and tree life also die. Reduction of water in streams and lakes happens quite frequently in areas where aquifers are used for agricultural needs. Approximately 60% to 75% of the life found in riparian ecosystems is contingent upon adequate availability of groundwater. It can lead to not only a reduction in water in streams and lakes but to their elimination. Natural water tables are dropping. When we cause drops in water table depth, it eliminates the only buffer for thousands of plant and animal species, and thus we indirectly become a cause for the death of riparian ecosystems through our choice to eat meat. Eating meat has vast tentacles of murder far beyond the simple act of eating an animal's body.

Increased Pumping Costs Means Additional Creation of GHG

When our neighbor's well went from 50 feet to 145 feet, she experienced what is happening in California's San Joaquin valley. Many farmers who use the San Joaquin aquifer would love to have wells to irrigate their farm lands at depths of 145 feet. Some wells today extend to a depth of 1,000 feet and a cost of $1.5 million. Some need to install a saline extraction facility because the water being pulled up from this depth was too salty. Whenever we need to pump from further down in the ground to get water to the surface, our electricity costs go up, too. And since a great deal of electricity comes from fossil fuel, this creates more climate change gas, further linking farming and meat eating to this issue. [221] [222]

San Joaquin Subsidence – What Comes Up Must Go Down

San Joaquin Valley is the poster child for subsidence and is considered the largest alteration of the earth's surface by humans.[223] Subsidence is a man-made phenomenon which occurs when we pump parts of an aquifer dry. The shale rock layers, which by nature have many gaps between them, collapse due to weight, gravity, and the removal of the water filling these gaps. This collapse causes the surface directly above to subside or drop. While this happens ever so gradually over time, ½ inch per month in San Joaquin, it can cause many problems with land structures such as pipelines, bridges, and roads, but especially to the aquaduct system in California built to deliver surface water from rivers and lakes.[224] This exacerbates the need, causing more groundwater to be pumped. One area, north of Bakersfield to Mendota, , sank 12 inches in a swath of land the size of Connecticut.

This area is predicted to drop a total of 17 feet by 2060. There is an excellent photo which explains subsidence in California's San Joaquin valley visually.[225] [226] [227] [228] [229]

The sign in the photo marked 1925 is 28 feet above the man standing next to the pole, scientist Joseph Poland:

water.usgs.gov/edu/gallery/landsubsidence-poland.html

Selenium Contamination

When we drill too deep in our obsession to find more fresh water, we also cause selenium contamination. When drought occurs in California, the subsidence increases; wells go deep and wide, and then cross-contamination can occur in the form of selenium. While we, humans and wildlife alike, all need a little selenium in our diets, too much is toxic. Selenium contamination of our drinking and crop-irrigation water harms us and wildlife by causing a higher accumulation in our tissues and in the ecosystem food chain.[230] Bioaccumulated selenium in aquatic food chains can cause many severe reproductive failures and teratogenic abnormalities in fish and other animals. Teratogenic agents can disturb the development of embryos and fetuses by halting the pregnancy or producing a congenital malformation (a birth defect).[231] [232] [233] [234] [235] When we choose to eat meat, dairy, and eggs, we also choose to tie ourselves to this aspect of environmental destruction. Selenium contamination is a condition of which we are a cause when we choose to eat animal products.

North China Plain

This overusage of groundwater is not a phenomena relegated to the US only but is happening globally. The

North China Plain is similar to the Ogallala aquifer in many ways. It spans a huge region in China and is the most fertile agricultural area in all of the country. And just like the Ogallala and San Joaquin it is also being drained faster than it is replenished, with its water table dropping 10 feet per year. It is also predicted to go dry if changes are not made soon.

This is in great part due to China's demand for more milk and meat products—and this demand is in a direct collision course with the needs of the overall population, 70% of which rely on groundwater as their primary drinking water source. This is all very frightening, as it leads to an uncertain future for one of the most heavily populated, economically valued agricultural areas of the world. [236] [237] [238] [239] [240] [241]

Misdirected Blame

While researching this topic of aquifers, agriculture usage, and water scarcity, what struck me as a funny was the fact that rarely was our diet discussed in mainstream media, when it comes to meat, dairy, and eggs. Many articles point the finger at California almonds, but very few articles point to dairy, which uses extravagant amounts of water in California. Missing from the conversation is the glass of milk, pork chop on our plate, burger at lunch, and eggs at breakfast. This is mystifying as 70% California's alfalfa crop, fed to dairy cows and livestock, is grown in San Joaquin Valley and it's the largest user of water.[242]

As has been shown, animal foods utilize high amounts of water. Approximately 1.8 million dairy cows in California each produce 2,550 gallons of milk.[243] [244] [245] [246] When we reflect it takes 30 gallons of water to produce a glass of milk—a substance clearly shown to have many associated health problems due to its high content of animal protein, hormones, pus, blood, and other substances foreign to human nutritional needs— shouldn't we take notice? And should not we (and mainstream media) question our usage of a precious, nonrenewable resource to manufacture what is considered to be a category 2 carcinogen?

Additionally, nowhere did the discussion flow to the amount of water which the 70 billion land animals we raise and kill each year drink. These 70 billion land animals drink a lot of water. Some drink as much as 70 times more water than we humans per day. There are 7 billion humans on the planet who each drink 0.64 gallon per day, and just accounting for the 1.4 billion cattle in the world, each of these animals needs between 10 and 45 gallons of water per day (Milking Cows: 35-45 gallons, Dry Cow: 20-30 gallons, Beef Cattle: 12 gallons).[247][248][249][250] Using an average of 27.5 gallons per animal means the cattle on our planet drink 38 billion gallons of water per day, whereas the humans drink 4.8 billion gallons of water per day. This doesn't even take into account the other 68 billion other farmed land animals who all consume water: pigs, goats, sheep, turkeys, and chickens.

What is missing is more discussion on the swapping of animal-based foods on our plates to plant products, and Dr. Oppenlander has the issue of sustainability and water consumption nailed when he points out:

> According to the EPA, the average household of three in our country consumes 50,000 gallons of water in one year for indoor use... However, this estimate does not include the water required to bring food to our table, which is by far the most

important factor in our water consumption. Consider that the average person in the United States consumes 206 pounds of meat in one yearn addition to 248 eggs and 616 pounds of dairy products. This equates to 405,000 gallons of water per person per year consumed just to support that animal product diet... Whenever there is a drought or water shortage anywhere in the country, does the government ever step up to declare a state or rationing meat or dairy? Of course not—but why not? [251]

When we consider it takes on average 40 gallons of water to produce a pound of lentils, peas, or beans whereas it takes, conservatively, 1,800 gallons of water to produce 1 pound of beef, we should take notice. Regardless of the measure, plant protein uses less water to produce than animal protein, and even it if used only 1 gallon more, it is wasteful, cruel, and indifferent to the needs of others we share this earth with, human and nonhuman. When we change to a WFPB diet, not only do we lower our water footprint but carbon footprint, too, and can help to make an impact on the lives of animals and human beings. Certainly, the plants and animals that desperately depend on groundwater in riparian ecosystems would be better able to survive. Certainly, the 2 billion people on the planet who depend on groundwater would be better able to survive and we would see health statistics improve. Lastly, with a change to a WFPB diet we can envision a world that uses water as a fully renewable resource and never runs out of it for anyone.

Interdependence

At the end of the day, we should pause and take note that we are all drinking from the same bowl of water. We all have straws poked into the earth's crust. We all have a piece of this issue, and when we sip from the underground well to consume animal products, we drink volumes more water than if we consumed plants only. When the underground water is gone, it's gone. We should all consider moving to a plant-based diet and thus use much less water. Mindfulness is an understanding that what we eat is tied to our water footprint and the life or death of trillions of sentient beings.

If we continue on our present course, by 2030 we will have a 40% water shortage on the planet.[252] [253] Today, close to a billion people are without an adequate fresh water supply and 2.5 billion people are without running water.[254] [255] In the U.S., 70% of all counties will face water risks by 2050, with 33% facing high or extreme risk.[256] [257]

We lament, and for good reason, hydraulic fracturing (fracking) for gas, whose process creates large amounts of methane to be emitted, uses billions of gallons of fresh water, and adds more to the global stockpile of fossil fuel for future burning. However, while fracking uses 70 to 140 billion gallons of fresh water annually in the U.S., agriculture uses 34 to 76 *trillion* gallons annually. Aquifers are going dry due to our love for meat, dairy, and eggs. Hospitals are full of sick humans because of our love of meat, dairy, and eggs, and the world is experiencing the sixth great extinction as we are on our way to destroying a majority of the other life forms on the planet due to our love for meat, dairy, fish, and eggs. Regardless of how much water it takes to raise commercial animals, it is all wasteful, unnecessary, and connected to agony, suffering, and death.

After fresh air, the most important component for life on earth is access to clean water. Water is necessary. We cannot sustain life on this earth without it. We all know this. The largest impact we can have on our water supply for all humans and other life on earth is to change our food choice. When we bear witness to this, we know that any use of water to raise animals is an abuse of resources. We know that any use of water to grow crops to feed to animals is an abuse of resources. We know any use of water to process and slaughter animals is an abuse of resources. We know the abuse of the Ogallala, San Joaquin, Great China Basin, and all other aquifers is directly caused by us and our food choice to eat animals. We do not need to eat animals to survive, but we and all wildlife need water. We have an impending water crisis. Our survival will depend the food choices we make. The first step is we all need to bear witness to this scientific fact.

Our perception changes when we bear witness. When we bear witness and understand how intertwined our food choices are to our own health, the health of animals, and the entire ecosystem of our precious planet, we have a responsibility to act. When we rest in full mindfulness with the information we now have, our perception can change. When our perception changes, we as spiritual practitioners with ethical hearts are called to action. When we are called to action to help the suffering of others, how will we respond?

Responsibility is the child of information, understanding, and bearing witness to suffering. Responsibility is the offspring of understanding the First

Noble Truth of suffering. The earth and all sentient life depend on us at this moment in time to understand that with the act of bearing witness there is a obligation to act. This is what an engaged spiritual practitioner from any background, Buddhist or otherwise, knows in their heart. When we fully embrace the amount of suffering our food choice causes, the great compassion of the Bodhisattva compels us to act.

Antibiotic-Resistant Superbugs

We have a national public health crisis, caused by overuse of antibiotics. *Consumer Reports* states, "The declining effectiveness of antibiotics has become a national public-health crisis, leading doctors and scientists to call for much more careful use of antibiotics so that disease-causing organisms don't become immune to them. But since approximately 80% of all antibiotics sold in the U.S. are used by the meat and poultry industry to make animals grow faster or to prevent disease in crowded and unsanitary conditions, both supermarkets and consumers can have a major impact on this problem through their purchasing decisions."[258] As our global appetite for meat increases, so too does the usage of antibiotics by the livestock industry; as our appetite grows so does theirs. The "careful use" of antibiotics being called for by doctors and scientists is in opposition to meat industry production, total output, and thus profit. The meat industry uses 29.9 million pounds of antibiotics per year,[259] fed directly to chickens, pigs, and other factory-farmed animals. Years ago it was found that feeding antibiotics to animals had a marked positive effect on the animal's ability to gain weight. The faster an animal gains weight, the faster it can get to market and the more profit is made. Additionally, antibiotics help limit the spread of disease on factory farms, where the conditions are unspeakably atrocious—nothing like the Old MacDonald's Farm from our childhood imagination. The gigantic antibiotic usage leads to resistant organisms. Once easily treated bacterial infections are now becoming harder to treat. These resistant forms of bacteria are showing up in our food.

On ground turkey, the Pew Foundation found that 78% of salmonella was resistant to one antibiotic and 50% was resistant to three or more antibiotics.[260] On chicken, almost 75% of the salmonella found were resistant to one antibiotic and half of the campylobacter bacteria (found on 95% of chicken) were resistant to tetracycline.[261]

Freebird Chicken

While at BuddhaFest, Washington DC, on a lunch break, I was in a salad shop having a great vegan salad with all the fixings: romaine, spinach, avocado, red onion, broccoli, edamame, carrots, craisins, apples, and balsamic vinaigrette, and I looked up at the wall. There was a sign that read:

"Freebird Chicken comes from local family farms in Pennsylvania. Plus, it's antibiotic-free, hormone-free and cage-free."

What a usage of of the word "free!" Leave it to the marketing folks to equate a 45-day life in captivity, to become a meal, with the meaning of the word "free." This bird may not have been in a cage, but I am sure the accommodations were not what it would have chosen for itself had it been actually free in nature. If we think we are eating a Freebird, we are forgetting someone in the equation who suffered and died.

Aside from that, the other thing that struck me was the tag of "free" when used in conjunction with antibiotics. This is a good thing, as this particular business was capitalizing on what is becoming common public knowledge: The animals we eat—which come from factory farms, also known as CAFOs (confined animal feeding operations)—are fed enormous amounts of antibiotics.

As discussed, the agribusiness industry found out years ago that if they fed animals antibiotics they would grow faster, but while growing faster means more profit, it is also true that overuse of antibiotics makes them less effective for humans. Life mutates. Bacteria mutate. Many of the new strains of bacteria the so-called superbugs, formerly cured with normal doses of methicillin or other antibiotics, are now resistant to these drugs and can be fatal.

One case in point is MRSA. MRSA stands for methicillin-resistant Staphylococcus aureus bacteria and is a form of staph resistant to all beta-lactam antibiotics (methicillin, penicillin, oxacillin, and amoxicillin). Why should we care? How about death, suffering, and potential mutation from resistance to immunity? If I asked you to answer a question about whether AIDS/HIV, E. coli, or MRSA were a greater risk for death, what would be your answer? If you didn't answer MRSA you were wrong. In the U.S., E. coli accounts for 100 deaths per year, AIDS/HIV for 16,000, and MRSA for 19,000.[262]

When you add this to the fact that there are an estimated 94,000 MRSA infections every year, which take increasing amounts of antibiotics to cure, this adds up to a lot of suffering on top of a lot of death.

Doug Gurian-Sherman from the Union of Concerned Scientists writes, "The massive use of antibiotics in CAFOs, especially for non-therapeutic purposes such as growth promotion, contributes to the development of antibiotic-resistant pathogens that are more difficult to treat. Many of the bacteria found on livestock (such as Salmonella, Escherichia coli, and Campylobacter) can cause food-borne diseases in humans. Furthermore, recent evidence strongly suggests that some methicillin-resistant Staphylococcus aureus (MRSA) and uropathogenic E. coli infections may also be caused by animal sources. These pathogens collectively cause tens of millions of infections and many thousands of hospitalizations and deaths every year." [263]

So what happens when you cram thousands of animals into tight quarters and feed them a steady diet of antibiotics to kill bacteria? As Dr. Ian Malcolm (Jeff Goldbaum) aphoristically stated in *Jurassic Park*, "Life finds a way." The bacteria mutate and become more resistant. As we continue to feed more and more antibiotics to animals crammed into the dirty petri-dish metal barns of factory farming, we culture more and more resistant forms of bacteria. The bacteria that survive the antibiotics have DNA structures that are more able and fit to survive. Indeed we set up a Darwinian experiment in each and every factory farm, killing off bacteria that are unable to survive and allowing those that can flourish to persist and mutate. It's survival of the fittest, evolutionary theory 101. As all life is programmed to find a way to survive, so too do bacteria find a way to survive by mutating and evolving. As they learn to defend themselves against the 29.9 million pounds of antibiotics they encounter, they become stronger and resistant. In Buddhist terms it's a function of impermanence; everything is changing, all the time, and it is a fabrication of our deluded minds to think we can control nature. Nature doesn't care about the economic whims and decisions to maximize profits made by the agriculture industry committees in conjunction with our government to supply our demand for harmful food.

Could MRSA become immune to all our antibiotics? Some think it's a possibility, as it's just a function of mathematical probability of getting the right combinations of chromosomes together and having enough of the bacteria survive. We do not want to envision a time when the bacteria become so resistant they are immune. There will not be a drug we can use to fight it, which will herald in a very sad time, with deaths from MSRA infections skyrocketing out of control.

What should we do? 1) Stop eating animals, and 2) curtail usage of antibiotics except for only the most critical need.

If we eat meat, fish, dairy, and eggs, we are part of the problem by supporting the industry which contributes to the declining effectiveness of antibiotics and further mutation of superbugs from resistant to immune. We become a cause as it is our purchases which fund the 29.9 million pounds of antibiotics to be fed directly to farmed animals.[264]

Norway in the mid-'70s did a reversal and changed the way medicine approaches this problem, rejecting unrestrained usage of antibiotics. According to Jon Barron, "Norwegian doctors now prescribe fewer antibiotics than any other country in the world. Quite simply, this prevents people from developing resistance to the antibiotics, while at the same time prevents the bacteria from developing resistant strains. How well does it work? Penicillin is still effective and prescribed for many infections in Norway!"[265] [266]

We all expect the FDA and our government to protect us. Unfortunately, they believe in a voluntary approach to industry antibiotic usage for agribusiness. But when voluntary cutting of antibiotic use reduces profit...nothing happens. Subsequently the meat industry is for the most part continuing to feast away on antibiotic usage and send out tainted meat to grocery shelves laden with a variety of antibiotic-resistant bacteria.

The contamination is so widespread that we have a 50/50 shot at encountering contaminated products from our groceries, many which carry MRSA, and all of which could cause us to become very ill and even die if not handled properly.[267] Don't contaminate your kitchen with raw meat and poultry drippings; it could be life threatening. Here in Michigan, a study found that the selling of beef, chicken, and turkey which contain *methicillin-resistant Staphylococcus aureus* bacteria is a common practice.[268] This study found that 20-25% of the chicken, turkey, and beef tested positive for MSRA.

Fortunately, we can make a simple change that provides a low-cost, straightforward solution: Become vegan. Vegans do not add to this problem, since they don't use animal products. Vegans cut the root cause of this market-driven problem because vegetables do not grow faster by being injected with or fed antibiotics. When there is no demand and no profit, the industry will shrink accordingly and transform, becoming a market for only people. That's what business does, it aligns with the market and customers. It's up to us to be better customers.

Appendix C: An Interview with Dr. Richard Oppenlander

I had the honor of discussing sustainability with Dr. Richard Oppenlander, author of two groundbreaking books, *Food Choice and Sustainability* and *Comfortably Unaware,* which are endorsed as a "must read" by Ellen DeGeneres, Dr. Jane Goodall, and Dr. Neal Barnard.

Dr. Oppenlander is a consultant and researcher, and a much sought after lecturer. He also serves as an advisor to municipalities in the U.S. and to world hunger projects that are designing programs from his model of multidimensional sustainability.

Since the early 1970s, Dr. Oppenlander has studied the effect our food choices have on our health and the environment. He is president and founder of an organic vegan food production company and education business, as well as the founder of the nonprofit organization, Inspire Awareness Now.

This interview is an update on the issues of sustainability and global depletion—as it relates to climate change, the loss of land and freshwater, and devastation of our oceans,. One of the most important points Dr. Oppenlander candidly discusses is the imminent and narrowing time lines we face in terms of resolution. Our oceans temperatures are rising faster than the IPCC prediction models due to fossil fuel usage (gas, oil, and animal agriculture). One of the most accelerating gases is methane whose upward slope is frightening. The single largest source of methane is from raising livestock. We are running out of time to make the necessary changes required for much of the life on earth, including the survival of our own species. According to Dr. Oppenlander we could eliminate today all fossil fuel usage as it relates to industry and still not meet our goals for greenhouse gas reductions due to just animal agriculture.

He weighed in on the subject of Goodland and Anhang's report of livestock being the cause of 51% of global GHG (Greenhouse Gas) as used in the movie *Cowspiracy,* which has been under fire as an inflated figure. He explained one issue with their calculation but also pointed out how incorrect the EPA and UN figures are on the amount of GHG animal agriculture puts into our global atmosphere. While Goodland and Anhang's figure may be a little inflated, the EPA and UN under-report due to pressure from livestock/animal agriculture committee members (who are motivated by financial incentives).

One of his main themes is the impending death of our oceans due to fishing. Globally we have 5 million fishing vessels on our oceans while only 1% of our oceans are monitored. This essentially means we are continuing down the road of extinction for all species. He points out that leaving fish in the ocean is the best thing we can do to help sequester GHG (as they sequester up to 2 gigatons of GHG emissions per year).

Of critical need for us to understand and implement, is that a plant-based diet is the best and most sustainable option for our bodies, the animals, and the earth. Food choice is the most significant component in the creation of a more sustainable and healthy planet, without which we will likely not reach a point of sustainability. Global awareness and immediate adoption of a fully plant-based diet and associated agricultural systems are necessary to achieve the highest level of relative sustainability.

Please see Appendix C for the full interview.

Privileged Suffering and the Protein Filter

"The Suffering of Our Privilege,"[269] a blog post by Cameron Conaway, speaks to the overabundance we have in the U.S., the shock of re-entry after being abroad for a few years and the suffering we feel over trivial issues in spite of our affluence when compared to poorer nations. In this piece, Conaway compares his living in Thailand for 3 years with coming back to his home in the States during the Thanksgiving holiday. In Thailand, he was consistently confronted with the brutal realities of unsafe work that threatens death and/or crippling injury on a daily basis, with HIV running rampant and disabled children sold as sex slaves. While in a U.S. department store, he reflects on overhearing arguments about the shortage of Christmas tree styles, the lack of Gucci purse variety, and other inane discussions that occur in our society of overabundance and consumerism. Shocking contrasts that exasperated him, as they do those of us who read his post. You can read it here:

goodmenproject.com/featured-content/cc-the-suffering-of-our-privilege/

He found inspiration in a podcast by Roshi Joan Halifax[270], in which she talks about her recent travels in Asia helping mountain people in Nepal. Her photos and the accounts of her annual Nepali travels are inspiring, compassionate, and uplifting. They force us to reflect on what we have versus what we need and can help put our lives in perspective. Halifax's account mirrors Conaway's in terms of the culture shock upon her return to Upaya Zen Center in New Mexico, where she contrasted the starving in Nepal in relation to serving nine special meals to the privileged at the Upaya center. She reflects:

> So many of you know I've gone to the Himalayas for decades, and it's so hard there. You know, in the mountains there's not one overweight person. People are functionally starving. That's why I said "We have nine special diets? And the kitchen is trying to cook nine different dishes, plus, for 60-some more of us?" And I went, "No, no. No. We can't do this."

> We have to really cut through to see what is essential, what is important, and to simplify. My backyard up at the refuge is beautiful mountains. You know, I can walk out my little hermitage door into such radiance. I don't need to travel halfway around the world. I go because I learn about resilience; I learn about tenderness, I also learn about what is essential and really important. Whatever is put before those mountain people...they eat, with gratitude. When I see where some of those children sleep...see all of those children with ringworms...and think about our kids and their crusty scalps and think about our clean heads and we're worried about one hangnail or another. It makes me want to weep, and not so much for them but, really, for us.

> Yeah, that's a kind of suffering they're in and it's raw. But the suffering of our privilege is another level of suffering. And what it is called in the literature is "adventitious suffering." Unnecessary suffering. We don't really have to do it this way. I feel we have in a certain way an inspiration from

the Buddha, who sat deeply, who probably actually didn't live too much differently than the mountain people we visit in Nepal. We say "Prince" but in actuality it was some little clan up in North India/Southern Nepal in a very funky area. I've been there. Still is. Malarial, stinking hot, not beautiful in the least.

And I look at our life and I say, "Hey, time for us to use the great and good karma we've been given to get over our biases now." And that is why we are practicing. So we can perceive not only those who are privileged and blind, but the mountain people and all beings as already awake, and to work for their realization of exactly that. I often think of Viktor Frankl in this regard, in the death camps saying, "We have one choice and that is the attitude with which we bring to our lives. To choose to not dwell in our biases, which are fed by our fears."

So this is why we practice."[271]

Going vegan a few years ago gave me the space to truly look at what I was doing, what I was eating and the chain of effects it has. Eating a simple hamburger, a piece of fish, or a chicken's breast is selfish from a resource perspective, health perspective, and spiritual perspective. It is a form of privileged suffering. Perhaps it is the ultimate form of privileged suffering.

I was reminded of Mahatma Gandhi's perspective as I thought about Halifax and Conaway's view: Measure all of what you do and decisions you make against their ability to help or hurt the poorest of the poor. This is a Bodhisattva's measure, too, to think about one's own actions and look to see if it helps or hurts those with the least.

Does being vegan fit the measure? And if so, how? And what is essential and simple? What type of attitude is brought forward based on choosing to eat meat, fish, dairy, and eggs or not? What attitude is brought when choosing to eat plants or not?

I believe Gandhi, the Buddha, and all people of reason and heart would agree that being vegan fits the measure, since it helps the poorest of the poor by using fewer resources, doing less harm, and allowing us the opportunity to share more. It honors not only humans but all sentient life and thus honors the poorest of the poor in every facet: innocent animals and humans. It honors the animals we consider food, who we allow to be invisible from us because of the sheer horror of being confronted with slaughter, dismemberment, and the despicably horrible conditions of factory farming. It honors the earth by harming it less through agriculture of plants for human consumption. It honors the diversity of life, insects, bees, and bugs of all kinds because it does not support millions of miles of monoculture plant life with the requisite toxic and lethal herbicides and pesticides used to grow GMO crops.

When we take ourselves off the pedestal of the so-called "top of the food chain," the nihilistic and egotistic idea that we can consume and exploit whatever and whomever simply because of tradition and sheer might, we realize might does not make right. In this created space we are opened to the truth of the privileged suffering of our traditional socially accepted meals and see that which causes us diseased states of body, mind, and spirit. Heart disease, cancers, diabetes, obesity, and osteoporosis are all forms of suffering related to our addiction to the privileged idea that we own other sentient species and can do what we please with them. The privilege of eating cows, pigs, chickens, fish, eggs, and dairy cause us privileged suffering with $300,000 heart surgeries and ensuing bags of medications which ruin our bodies and minds prematurely. The privilege of eating meat brings with it the privileges of obtaining certain cancers that run rampant in Western countries. The privilege of eating meat brings the suffering of diabetes, years of drugs, myriad other side effects, not to mention the disease causing our body to fail. The privilege of eating meat brings obesity. As we ingest meat causing 70 billion sentient land animals their death annually, they cause our suffering and death. As we cause their death, we cause the death of the entire planetary ecosystem, with millions of miles of monoculture fields of plants, replete with millions of tons of petrochemical fertilizers, usage of Roundup and other herbicides, and tons of pesticides all burning the soil and its ability to sustain life, that drains into our waterways, killing fish and countless other types of aquatic life, causing algae blooms and dead zones, heating the atmosphere, warming the earth toward the ultimate privileged suffering of global warming and the destruction of our habitat and its ability to sustain us. As we deplete the resources and life of the planet, we sow our own depletion and lives.

Eating meat in many ways was a bias for me, and I know it was fed by my own ignorance, delusion, and fear. I had incorrect information and thus feared getting sick if I didn't get enough protein, feared my body getting a disease, but mostly feared changing my traditions, habits, and tastes.

If we choose to eat plants, only plants, it is in a very real sense a compassionate act. We use less so we can share more. One study suggests the cattle population on earth consumes enough calories to feed 8.7 billion people.[272] [273] [274] Others suggest an additional 4 billion people could be fed if we started using the land we currently use to grow food for animals and switched to crops for human consumption.[275] [276] [277] On paper, we could end world hunger by feeding to people the food we grow and feed to animals. How much simpler could this be? Eat plants, and feed the world's hungry.[278] Eat plants, and animals will not be caged, chained, and corralled in factory farms. Eat plants, and rainforests will not need to be destroyed to grow plants to feed animals. Eat plants, and dead zones will begin to disappear. Eat plants, and the Western diseases of abundance will fade. Eat plants, and obesity will dissipate. Eat plants, and fish, coral reefs, and all species of sea life will rejuvenate. Eat plants, and we can slow climate change dramatically. Eat plants, a simple, compassionate solution.

The poor nomads and mountain people of the world have no choice. It's a choice of survival or death for them. They eat what they can get. It's been this way most of the time we humans have been on the planet. It's only in more recent time, the last 10,000 thousand years or so, in which agricultural methods and herding have allowed us to grow more than we need to subsist. We have abundance. However, over this time herding culture has numbed us to enslavement, killing, and our connection to the feminine. As, author of the World Peace Diet, Will Tuttle states, "the inner feminine is our intuition, our sensitivity, and our ability to sense the profound interconnectedness of events and beings, and it is vital to peace, wisdom, joy, intelligence, creativity, and spiritual awakening. With every baby calf stolen from her mother and killed, with every gallon of milk stolen from enslaved and broken mothers, with every thrust of the raping sperm gun, with every egg stolen from a helpless, frantic hen, and with every baby chick killed or locked for life in a hellish nightmare cage, we kill the sacred feminine within ourselves." [279]

How did this happen and what does it have to do with today's world? Herding culture is perhaps the quintessential historic form of structural violence and seems to be where today's power, in the hands of a few, got its start. We know herding brought wealth, security, and power before money was invented. In fact money in the old world was even named after a certain number of animals. A Roman denarius, a small silver coin, was equal to 10 asses. And we know that the latin word capita means head, as in a head of cattle, sheep, or goat, and thus capitalism is related to herding animals. It also brought us much more negativity than positivity. We learned about slavery by enslaving gentle animals. We learned about manipulation of the feminine species through killing off of males and the selective the breeding of animals.

We learned to have disregard for the earth by enslaving and raising herds of animals, which depleted the land of resources. This was one of the first forms of extractivism, and when the land was depleted by unnaturally large herds foreign to the ecology, wars were fought to take lands from other people whose land was not despoiled. Herding led to wealth for a few, greed, and violence. The wars led to the capture of the other people's animals and their human population. Slavery was born, since it is a small leap from enslaving animals to enslaving other people. Wars against other herding cultures can be linked to much of the injustice in the world today toward both humans and animals alike. If we can kill an innocent animal, a trusting being, for the sake of food and profit it's a small step forward to consider people from another tribe, region, or skin color as different. Our sensibilities toward females, racism, and the earth have been dulled to the point of a total lack of awareness to the beings which we cook and place in our bodies. We don't make connection anymore we are so blinded. While we no longer see the animals in billions roaming the landscape because our herds are behind closed doors in factory farms, we know they exist if we choose to be aware, since we still see animals on our plates three times daily.

Business marketing and bad science has falsely brought us to believe we need to consume animal food to be healthy. Agribusiness, corporate profits, and governmental support have paid for the continued dulling of our senses, promoting or creating bias, and belief in the illusion of humans as separate from nature and animals.

Nomads, mountain folk, and inner city poor with low incomes and living in perhaps a food desert (an economic injustice in and of itself) have limited choice, but we who are blessed to have been born with more prosperity are free to choose. We can choose to become educated. We can decide to change. We can pause. We can learn not to immediately react to cravings for flesh foods, dairy, and eggs. We can reflect on our true inner motivations, and then we can choose wisely, mindfully, prudently, with health for ourselves, and compassion for all beings. We can remember that with privilege comes responsibility. Or we can continue with callousness, tradition, and a mindless abjuration of reality based upon our normal rutted reactivity and its inherent cruelty. What we choose has a direct impact on the poor people who have no choice. What we choose has a direct impact on future generations of those we say we love and care for. What we choose can either help the world heal or cause more destruction.

As Shantideva informs us in "The Bodhisattva's Way of Life":

> O you who wish to guard your minds,
> I beseech you with folded hands:
> Always exert yourselves to guard,
> Mindfulness and alertness!
> People who are disturbed by sickness
>
> Have no strength to do anything (useful),
> Likewise those whose minds are disturbed by confusion
>
> Have no strength to do anything (wholesome). [280]

As a Buddhist practitioner I try to practice, to find my own thorns and biases. I try to unhook from my own mad confusion that causes suffering and detachment from my true self and thus all others. Being vegan has given me some tools to become more awakened about my choices. I now know how resource-intensive meat, fish, dairy, and eggs are and how much suffering is involved, as eating them leads to global depletion, climate change, and issues of social justice. I no longer choose resource-intensive items to feed my body. I eat plants. I eat grains. I eat fruit. I eat as close to raw as I can get. I shop at the local Oakland County farmers market and eat/buy local whenever possible. This allows me to save on water, gas, and transportation for myself and the planet. It allows me to nourish myself and stop supporting the pollution of the planet by chemicals and herbicides. It allows me to do my part to help not only the animals but the entire planet.

If we choose to be part of the growing global vegan community, it gives us the option to help end world hunger. It gives us the option to share our abundance. It gives us space to relieve a little suffering in the world. It disconnects us from the structural violence built into the fabric of our culture: factory farming and the unnecessarily unhealthy polluting practice of eating sentient beings. In doing so we come to lead simpler lives, to be less confused and biased, and more present.

Resource Utilization – The Inefficiency of Turning Plants into Meat

The feed-conversion ratio is the efficiency of an animal to eat food and turn it into body mass: bones, fat and muscle.[281] The agriculture industry measures this very closely and works hard to find ways to improve the ratio. The better the ratio the more profits are made. But the reality of feeding animals grain is this: We get less food out than the food we put in. We waste precious resources. Whenever we choose to eat meat we choose to squander food, hurt the planet, and ourselves. It takes 7 to 16 pounds of grain to make 1 pound of beef[282]. While 800 million or more humans suffer every day from hunger and malnutrition, Americans eat an average of 200 pounds of meat, fish, dairy, and eggs per year, consuming unhealthy animal protein in large quantities. [283] [284] So while close to a billion people functionally starve each day, we in the West overeat and feed grain to animals in a wasteful manner, since grain eaten directly by people would go much further.

A pound of beef contains 117 grams of protein, whereas the 7 pounds of corn required to produce a pound of beef contain 283 grams of protein and 7 pounds of soybeans have 1,134 grams of protein. This is a waste of a lot of protein which could be eaten directly by the billion or so men, women, and children who go hungry every day. This negative usage of our resources has grown and continues to grow as our appetite for meat is rising with the population and greater affluence. In the 1950s global production of meat was 44 million tons. In 2016 it has grown to well over 350 million US tons.[285] [286] By 2050, meat production is expected to rise to 501 million US tons.

To make matters worse, one third of the food grown in poor countries is fed to animals. As Dr. Richard Oppenlander states, "Realize that 82% of the world's starving children live in countries where food is fed to animals, which are then killed and eaten by more well-off individuals in developed countries like the U.S., UK, and in Europe. One-fourth of all grain produced by third-world countries is now given to livestock, in their own country and out."[287] As Buddhists, humanitarians, ecologists, spiritual practitioners, and friends of the earth, we should all become aware of what we are doing by our choices. Our food choices have costs. What we do when we eat meat is we accept animals as our protein; we place ourselves in a privileged status to use their bodies and lives to nourish ourselves. We use animals as factories to produce protein. But this is a reverse protein proposition, because it is very inefficient; we're basically throwing food away when we choose to eat meat. Instead of eating a pound of beef, if we ate the equivalent protein in soybeans, we could feed an additional eight people.

If we say we care about world hunger and the environment but continue to eat meat, fish, dairy, and eggs, are we being honest with ourselves? The more caring action would be to eat 1 of the 7 pounds of beans and share the other 6 pounds with six other families. While we are turning off lights, driving more fuel-efficient cars, and recycling, we might as well change our minds and eat a WFPB diet. It is hypocritical to say we want to save the planet and continue to eat meat, fish, dairy, and eggs. It is the same as saying "I love animals," when there is a steak, chicken, or pig on your plate. It is the same has believing in humane slaughter when we know slaughter cannot be humane by definition. We cannot truly care for the planet and eat animals.

But some still believe animal protein is a complete protein, a superior protein. As discussed by Sherry Morgado (see Interview with a Vegan Buddhist Nutritionist), Frances Moore Lappe's erroneous assumption in *Diet for a Small Planet* gave birth to that myth.[288] The truth is plant protein is just as good as animal protein and we don't need to eat different plants in combination to meet our body's protein requirements. Our bodies can synthesize all the missing amino acids in plants for us.

There are very high oil/energy costs associated with meat. Michael Pollan, former editor for *Harper's Magazine* and a famous food writer, purchased a steer for tracking purposes, and from birth to slaughter, the steer indirectly used 100 gallons of oil.[289] Other estimations put the amount of oil used to bring a steer to market higher, at 284 gallons.

But oil is not the only cost. There is the cost of our military in the Middle East and elsewhere to protect oil and business interests. There are the water pollution and water usage costs. There are the greenhouse gas and climate change costs. There are the costs of deforestation (related to climate change) and loss of biodiversity. There are the costs of growing corn, soy, and alfalfa, using ever increasing tracts of land and fresh water supplies. There are the costs of dead zones in the oceans. There are the costs of antibiotic usage, their declining effectiveness, and the incubation of resistant microbes. There are the costs of unnecessary hormones in our food. There are the costs to our health. There are the costs of eroded topsoil, fish kills, displaced wildlife, destroyed vegetation, and killed wildlife to protect farmer interests.

All these costs could be eliminated or greatly reduced if we just ate plants. Plants are abundant sources of protein and cause much less suffering to all. We should eat only plants and realize that the privileged status we occupy, the throne of food we have put ourselves upon, is costly and tilting like the Tower of Pisa, and the fall we are going to take will hurt a lot. Shouldn't we become educated and mindful and get over our bias? Shouldn't we just teach ourselves to eat only plants?

The Dharma

How can a bhikkshu (nun or monk), who hopes to become a deliverer of others, himself be living on the flesh of other sentient beings? Pure and earnest bhikkshus, if they are earnest and sincere, will never wear clothing made of silk, nor wear boots made of leather, because it involves the taking of life.

~ The Buddha, The Shurangama Sutra

Hell Realms

Factory Farming

Don't know anything about factory farming? Google the term. Read about it. Review some of the thousands of videos taken by brave undercover activists who want us to know the truth. Mercy for Animals, GaryTV, and PETA have many illuminating videos. Unable to bear watching these videos? If you eat meat, fish, dairy, and eggs and call yourself a spiritual practitioner but are incapable of tolerating these videos, should you not ask yourself why the truth of what you support is so abhorrent?

Factory farms are hell realms designed for only precise optimization of inputs and outputs: food/water and living beings. The idea behind them is to utilize as little space, time, and money to grow an animal from birth to market. Time is money. Feed is money. Wages are money. Each square foot, pound of grain, antibiotic, and waste lagoon, not to mention working standards, are designed for getting an animal to market. An animal's natural instincts, needs, wants, and happiness are always superseded by profit. Animals endure hellish conditions, never seeing the sun, smelling fresh air, or doing anything that is natural to them. In many cases, the first time they ever feel the wind on their skin is in the slaughterhouse transport. They are simply commodities and we have engineered a scientific way of giving them as little space, food, water, and air as possible without killing them prior to their slaughter. This book doesn't deal with factory farming in depth, but let's review briefly the short life of pigs, egg laying chickens, broiler chickens, and dairy cows.

Pigs

Pigs are highly sentient. Pigs are able to solve problems, love to play, have emotions, and display individual personalities. They can use mental discrimination with a comprehension of symbolism and are able to anticipate what is next in an event and prepare for it. They have numerical understanding, can understand pointing actions by humans and show the existence of emotion and empathy. They have been taught to play computer games and can recognize their own faces in a mirror. They have their own sense of self. Their personality structure compares with humans and other species of animals and there is a general consensus that pigs are the third smartest animal on the planet after humans. What we do to these animals so that we can eat them is unconscionable.

Breeding sows live their short lives in gestation cages where they are unable to even turn around. They

give birth to 10 to 12 piglets in farrowing pens, where they nurse their young. The normal nursing time for baby pigs is 12 weeks, but this is cut down to 2-4 weeks so the breeding sow can be impregnated again. This process occurs over and over until they reach the age of 3 or 4 years and then they are slaughtered. One-fifth of all young pigs die from trauma and disease, and those that live are tagged and castrated without anesthesia. Soon they are placed in metal pens to live their short lives. At 4–6 months old they are put on metal slaughterhouse transports, generally 200 per truck, and sent to their deaths. Seeing the sun and breathing their first fresh air, pigs are known to die of heart attacks from the joy of running for the first time, out of the jail cells. At the slaughterhouse they are routinely beaten off the truck into a holding area, prodded, and zapped into the so-called stunning area. They are incapacitated in some fashion, with a bolt to the head, electric shock, or gassed, and then they are hung up by a hind leg and their throats are cut. Many are still fully conscious. After they bleed out, they go into the scalding hot tanks to remove hair and other viscera, and again many still are fully conscious. In the U.S. alone, 115 million pigs are killed each year. All of them had intelligence, personality, and a life; however, none of them ever knew kindness nor wanted to die. [290]
[291] [292] [293] [294] [295] [296] [297]

Chickens

When I first started volunteering at a local animal sanctuary I was hoping to be able to work with the cows, pigs, and goats—I had zero interest in spending time with the chickens. I thought chickens were dirty, uninteresting animals. The first time I was asked to clean the chicken coop I was very disappointed, but I went anyway. I'll never forget the adorable bantam rooster I met that first day—his crow broke midway through and he was just the tiniest, cutest little dude I had ever seen. Within 30 minutes of hanging out in the coop I was mesmerized by these chicken-people who I had once thought were nothing special. I'm so grateful to have lived the life I've lived, to be able to know and develop relationships with people not of the human form...

> Tami Seegrist McMinn, Co-Founder, Director of Outreach and Engagement at Humanity For Animals

Chickens are thought of as mere automata and widgets in factory farming; however, they are living, breathing, sentient beings that think, have compassion and empathy, can reason, and have emotions. Chickens have needs and wants, one of which is to enjoy their lives. Chickens form bonds and can recognize one another. Chicks take guidance from their mothers and take cues from each other. They can speak to one another in their own language and have more than 24 different vocalizations. Baby chicks talk to their mother before hatching to let them know they are cold, so mom can move the egg, and they even purr in the egg, letting mom know they are OK. By the time they do hatch, they know their mom's voice from all the communication.[298] [299] [300]

Layers

Chickens in the West have been bred to come in two varieties: layers and broilers. If you were hatched in an egg-layer hatching facility and end up on a CAFO you will live a life of depression and misery. The first experience a female hatchling has is their beak being seared off with a hot knife to remove the sharp end. Beaks, more sensitive than human fingertips, are seared off hens so they will not peck cell mates in the battery cage when the stress of living with 7 to 12 others, each on the size of an 8.5 x 11 inch piece of paper, becomes too difficult. If the hatchling survives the debeaking ordeal and does not starve to death due to the horrendous pain in the nerve endings of their beak, they will be caged for life.

If you are a male hatchling (50% are male), you will be suffocated in garbage bag, ground up alive, or gassed on the spot (since you cannot lay eggs and are thus are of no use in the industrial egg complex). There are 150,000 male chicks killed in the U.S. each day in this manner. [301]

As a surviving female egg layer, your entire life will be lived in a metal shed, inside a battery cage, standing and sleeping on the wire bottom of the cage. You will be in semi-darkness, the light manipulated to maximize your productive capability. Wild chickens produce 10 to 15 eggs per year, but you will produce 300 eggs per year. When your production fails in a year or two, you will be considered "spent," as you can no longer produce eggs fast enough. Your body is devastated by this time, as your muscle tissue was never able to grow correctly, crammed as you have been so closely with others. You have severe muscle loss, you probably have spinal cord deterioration, you may be partially paralyzed, and you are severely calcium deficient. Your bones are brittle from all the eggs you have produced and lack of exercise. You will have what is known as Cage Layer Fatigue Syndrome, a known side effect of your incarceration. Around you may be other hens whose paralysis is complete; their bodies so immobilized from spinal cord deterioration they can no longer move and get to food or water. Approximately 450 million egg-laying hens are slaughtered every year in the U.S. when their production falls.

But you say, "I eat organic eggs which are more humanely raised." Nothing could be further from the truth. Many undercover videos show the horror of organic egg facilities, where chickens have a little more room, air, and sunlight than traditional factory-farmed hens. A recent report details the sad conditions for chickens in the largest organic layer facility in the U.S. where 1.6 million hens live in nine barns (each containing 180,000 beings) in conditions of more than three hens per square foot of floor space. Please put yourself in the place of these USDA organic hens and choose to live in your closet for the next week with two or three of you best friends, 24/7, without access to fresh air, sunlight, or bathrooms. Organic food and water will be provided, but that's it. One in ten organic eggs are supplied to the U.S. market by this one facility, whose label eases the conscious of consumers but does nothing about the true hellish conditions for hens. [302 303 304 305]

Broilers

We kill more broiler chickens annually in the U.S. than there are humans on the planet—9 billion. These chickens live in huge, metal, windowless sheds, each holding 20,000 to 30,000 birds. They live their short lives (42–45 days) in horrendous conditions on manure- and urine-soaked wood shavings which remain unchanged through several flocks. The ammonia buildup causes a disease named ammonia burn, which afflicts the birds so badly they cry out in pain when they rub their eyes with their wings. These chickens, packed by the thousands into these closed sheds, are further accosted as salmonella and campylobacter bacteria grow and spread infecting them.

Broiler chickens have been genetically bred to have extra-large muscles in their breasts and thighs. They grow so fast that many cannot walk or stand by the time they are deemed ready for slaughter. They are lame and miserable from the pain. They exhibit respiratory, gastrointestinal, and blood diseases. When they reach a market weight of 5 pounds, still mere babies, they are sent to slaughter. This process sees them handled roughly at the farm when collected, as they are sucked into chicken-catching machines, which can vacuum 7,000 birds per hour. Chickens can travel up to 12 hours in jam-packed crates through winter's extreme cold and summer's heat all without food or water. When they arrive they may sit freezing or dying from heat in the truck until the facility is ready up to another 12 hours. If they are sick or too injured to be used for food they are routinely dumped alive into mass graves. Rough handling continues at the slaughterhouse as they are ruthlessly grabbed by their legs (many of which break in the process) and they are turned upside down, shackled, pulled through an electrified water bath for stunning, and have their throats slit. The rate of slaughter can be so high, legally up to 140 per minute, many are completely conscious when their throats are slit and many miss the blade and are then scalded alive. In the U.S. 17,000 chickens are slaughtered per minute, 24/7. Birds do not fall under the humane slaughter act and at the rate of kill which is standard at slaughterhouses, it is impossible to slay benevolently (if there could ever be such a thing without the consent of the one being slain). [306] [307] [308] [309] [310] [311] [312] [313] [314] [315] [316] [317] [318] [319]

Dairy Cows

The life of a dairy cow is very similar to the life of an egg-layer hen and one of the saddest for any animal. Dairy cows only produce milk after they give birth following 9 months of gestation. Milk, we should remember, comes from mothers, not from cows. Dairy cows are forcibly impregnated year after year to keep them lactating. For a human this would be considered rape. Just like human mothers, they are aware of their "baby" inside, who moves, kicks, and lives. A natural bond is formed, but just after giving birth to their offspring they are cruelly separated within 24 hours. For a human this would be considered kidnapping and theft. This process creates so much sadness and grief for both mother and calf that mothers are known to bellow for days. Calves are so bewildered, frightened, and continually looking for their mother who is nowhere to be found that they are known to stop eating. We don't need to be scientists to understand this process creates a huge amount of stress and negative emotional states.

There are approximately 9 million dairy cows in the U.S., and due to the repeated impregnation every 9 months there is a huge surplus of calves. Male calves are not ground up like newly born hatchlings in the egg industry but nonetheless they are useless, since they don't produce milk, and are thus are sold for veal. A percentage of the female calves become dairy cows, and the rest are also sold as veal. Veal calves have short, miserable lives chained or penned in small houses where they cannot move very much, in order to keep their flesh tender. They are slaughtered very soon after birth. This practice occurs on so-called humane and organic farms, too, so don't be misled to think there is such a thing— male calves cannot produce milk on humane organic farms either.

The contemporary dairy cow has been bred to produce two to four times more milk than historical volumes and her body cannot cope with this for more than 5 years. This breeding for excessive milk production and living indoors on concrete for most of her life leads to the diseases of mastitis (a bacterial infection of their udders) and lameness. They are in pain for most of their short lives. When they cannot stand or become pregnant again, or when their milk production falls below acceptable standards, they are sent to slaughter. Just as an egg-layer hen is considered "spent," so is a dairy cow at this stage. Spent cows also occur on so-called humane organic farms, since there is no financial motive to keep a cow alive after she cannot produce milk.

Cows normally can live for 20–25 years, but the cycle of forced impregnation, kidnapped calves, life indoors on concrete, lactating year after year without a break, and never being able to act on their natural social behaviors takes its toll on the well-being of these sentient beings. Don't be misled by the industry marketing, there are no gently sloping, bright emerald fields and peaceful grazing in the countryside. Happy cows do not exist in the dairy industry, as the majority of dairy products in the U.S. come from factory farms. In the factory farm environment cows suffer and rarely, if ever, see the sun and feel a gentle breeze on their skin the end all dairy cows end up with their throats slit, hung by a leg in a slaughterhouse as a supply to the ground beef industry which gets 20–40% of their meat from the dairy industry. Vegetarians, as consumers of dairy, are part of this cause and effect system. Dairy cows live horrendous lives of misery and suffering, all for our love of their calves' milk in the form of yogurt, ice cream, and milk. They did not choose the life of enslavement. They do not choose to die to become hamburger. [320 321 322 323 324 325 326 327]

Christian Hell Realms

Growing up in a 1960s Roman Catholic household, I learned about the concept of hell at an early age in catechism class at St. Rita's in Detroit. The strict nuns who taught me were very clear about its attributes. It was hot, painful, and evil, an appropriate place for sinners to spend eternity. Later I read much of Dante's *Inferno,* which explained more about hell, his visions and the one shared by the Church at that time. It's a place which creates tremendous fear. I was taught at a young age that you end up there based on God's ultimate decision for you, a decision which is final and eternal, a one-way ticket to never-ending suffering damnation.

Buddhist Hell Realms

I was surprised to find out that hell also exists for Tibetan Buddhists and that there are more similarities than differences between the two versions. In fact, Buddhist teachers describe 18 distinct versions of hell, each with its own unique set of sufferings. However, there are two distinct differences between Buddhist and Christian hell: First, in Buddhism you go to hell based on your own negative actions that hurt yourself and others, and second, it is not eternal. No one externally judges you; your actions alone cause the result of hell rebirth. In Buddhism, the hell realm to which you go is based on how severe the negative actions were that you committed. Killing with intent, desire, and satisfaction gets you into a worse hell (and for longer) than killing without intent, desire, and satisfaction. Stealing, lying, cheating, and other negative activities are less offensive than killing and land you in one of the less severe hell realms with a smaller amount of misery.[328] [329] [330] [331]

During my first Buddhist retreat in 1997, I remember Gelek Rimpoche discussing hell realms and stating: "This Lam Rim teaching was traditionally given to people who already accepted life after death. Normally they would say: After death you do not disappear, you will continue. Granted that you do continue, your continuation will be either a good one or a bad one. What the bad one is...hell rebirth." [332]

And just as in Catholicism, hell is taught as a real place in Buddhism. Gelek Rimpoche continued, "The hell realms are real, for sure. The sufferings of the hell experience in human life are also real... I'm not telling you a fairy tale story. Avoid hell rebirth. It is in our hand right now because we are responsible for what we do. Since I am responsible for myself, and you are responsible for yourself, we can do or undo right now. But if we don't talk about the hell realms at all, and we talk as if everything is wonderful and beautiful, there is no difference between 'love and light' and actual reality."[333]

So hell realms, *naraka* in Sanskrit, are real places according to Tibetan Buddhist teachings, and there are eight hot, eight cold, and two nearby the human realm. The hells also have a hierarchy of best to worst, and are located one on top of another. Interestingly, they have locations, too. The hell of Continual Resurrection is located 32,000 yojanas[334] under Bodhgaya, India, with the other hot hells below it.

The eight hot hells are places we don't ever want to visit. For instance, Continual Resurrection is a place where all beings are armed with weapons. Everyone here is revived a hundred times a day after brutally killing others in combat. Eventually you are also mortally wounded, and when everyone in the combat is incapacitated and no longer able to wield a cudgel, sword, knife, or spear, you are revived. In this hell and all Buddhist hell realms, you don't die. You may have your head or limbs severed and can no longer fight, but you do not experience death, because it is your karma to be in this place. In Continual Resurrection, as soon as everyone is incapacitated, a booming voice comes over the battleground commanding all to arise and be born anew. Magically, each and every person is revived, healed, and angry. Then the vicious fighting recommences, and anything touched in this realm turns instantly into a weapon, immediately at your disposal.

Another of the hot hells is called Black Line or Black Thread.[335] It is very reminiscent of animal slaughter. In this place, hell beings draw lines on your body and you are cut, while alive, down each and every line. It is said you are put on a rack of some sort, tied down, drawn upon with a marker, and then cut, sawed, sliced in half from end-to-end into multiple pieces. As in all hell realms, these cut pieces still feel intense pain even when they are severed and detached from your body.

The next hell is Butcher's Hell, also called Assembled and Crushed or Crushing Hell, Samghata. In this hell, one finds oneself between two large rocks, like mountains, with the heads of the animals you have personally butchered in life appearing on the top of the rocks. According to Gelek Rimpoche, this hell "is one that butchers are supposed to experience. The animals that you butchered appear to you in this hell as huge mountains and smash you in between them. Then you revive, and it happens again."[336] So you are being mashed and pounded into a pulp, crushed over and over by mountains that have the essence of the sentient beings you killed in human life. Again in this hell you never really die; when the process is over, you are renewed to start again.

The next hot hell is named Lamentation, where one is put into a dwelling made of burning hot metal with no doors and is on fire both inside and out. Realizing you cannot find a way out, you despair and begin wailing and lamenting loudly. This hell is followed by Great Lamentation, Hotter Hell, Even Hotter Hell, and ending up with Vajra Hell.

Vajra hell, the last and deepest hell, is where you are roasted alive in a great oven of intense fire. This hell is also called Avici, "uninterrupted" or "no respite," because you never get a chance to rest. If you end up here, you simply see flames everywhere, in you, outside of you, in all directions. The suffering here is worse than the other hot hells, is the longest lasting, and is reserved for those who have committed the most horrible negativities.

Cold hells are aptly named according to the suffering one gets from each. Blisters or Goose Skin is one hell where your naked body lives and large blisters form on our skin. One account of it describes "a dark, frozen plain surrounded by icy mountains and continually swept by blizzards. Inhabitants of this world arise fully grown and abide lifelong naked and alone, while the cold raises blisters upon their bodies. The length of life in this naraka is said to be the time it would take to empty a barrel of sesame seeds if one only took out a single seed every hundred years."[337]

Another cold hell is Burst Blisters, where your skin cracks because of the intense cold. This is followed by Sneezing, Moaning, Frozen Jaw, Blue Lotus, Red Lotus, and lastly Mahapadma (the great lotus). In this last hell your body cracks into fragments everywhere, exposing your internal organs, which also crack and you become like a shattered lotus.

There are other hells which are said to be in close proximity to the human realm. Pabongka Rinpoche describes them in *Liberation in the Palm of Your Hand* as The Surrounding Hells, stating, "Round the outside of the hot hells, like the iron fence [that encircles this world system], there are four surrounding hells: the Fiery Trench, the Putrid Swamp, the Plain of Razor-Sharp Knives, and the Uncrossable Torrent."[338] These are all hells that beings who have spent time in one of the other worse hells, hot or cold, are able to escape to, as their karma weakens just before taking birth into a better realm. These are also hells where one can find oneself born straight into after life as a human. These places are just as brutal as the other hells. The Fiery Trench burns your legs as you try to cross for miles and miles, for years, only to escape and find yourself in the Putrid Swamp, where you sink up to your neck and are eaten by worms with teeth and beaks like birds, which peck holes into your body, leaving you looking like a colander. From the Putrid Swamp, one escapes to the Plain of Razor-Sharp Knives, only to hear loved ones at the top of a hill calling for you. Desiring to be with them, you walk and crawl naked and barefoot across vegetation as sharp as steel razors, penetrating and cutting you everywhere they touch. When you get to the top, you find that the loved ones you tried so hard to get to have disappeared and now are at the bottom of the hill, so you start the process all over again going down the hill, with the knives are all pointing at you once again. Like plants following the sun, they have somehow turned toward you and are waiting to cut you again. They are followed by the Uncrossable Torrent, a body of water that is mixed with fire that cooks your body like peas in a boiling pan.

Another Surrounding Hell Realm

As I read the accounts from undercover workers from Mercy for Animals and former workers in factory farming and slaughterhouses, it became apparent that there are many similarities between the hells in Buddhism and the modern commoditization of sentient beings in factory farms, animal slaughter, and animal testing/vivisection.

This, of course, is kept from the eye of the general public and thus along with our own wish to not become aware, we never learn about it.

The scalding torture of hell beings is akin to what we visit upon chickens and pigs still alive and being dunked into scalding hot water, fully conscious and fighting to stay alive.[339] They don't know why or where they are. They are just hanging upside down with other chickens. Their terror must be so great as they are fed into the hot boiling, roiling, chlorinated water, dunked and trying to breathe, trying to escape. Typical slaughterhouses kill so many animals per hour there is no way for them all to be given a painless death. Stunning is always improper, even when it operates as intended.

Black Line hell is no different from how a butcher makes the finest cuts of roast, chops, and steaks. It's not so different from what we put animals through in a slaughterhouse by electrocuting them, putting a metal pin into their brains, slitting their throats, all while they are still alive and conscious. If we killed them and then slaughtered them, their meat would have a lot of blood in it, and we don't like the taste of meat with blood in it (more evidence we are not true carnivores). Thus our food carcasses must be as free of blood as possible, and this means the heart must still be pumping to rid the body of blood. Just as a hell being's body is alive when he or she is slit, the heart of animals pumps out their blood and they actually die from exsanguination.[340] After exsanguination, the body of the animal is cut up into the various parts and packaged.

As in the Hotter Hell, impaling and beatings of various sorts using prods, sharp instruments poked at the animals, into their vagina, their anus, through the skin, or just beaten anywhere all happen at factory farms, during transport and at the slaughterhouse itself. This has been documented by PETA, Mercy for Animals, and many other organizations.

Gail A. Eisnitz, in her book *Slaughterhouse*, interviewed one who had worked in many slaughterhouses. In relation to pig production, he told her: "Hogs get stressed out pretty easy. If you prod them too much, they have heart attacks. If you get a hog in the chute that's had the shit prodded out of him and has a heart attack or refuses to move, you take a meat hook and hook it into his bunghole. You try to do this by clipping the hipbone. Then you drag him backwards. You're dragging these hogs alive, and a lot of times the meat hook rips out of the bunghole. I've seen hams— thighs—completely ripped open. I've also seen intestines come out. If the hog collapses near the front of the chute, you shove the meat hook into his cheek and drag him forward."

These chained, roped, or otherwise locked up beings are tortured against their will. They didn't ask to become someone's food. They were just born here. Much like we would be, if when we die we wake up in a hell realm with hell beings impaling us.

Skinning in a hell realm is a common torture, also, and this exists in every slaughterhouse. It is also part and parcel of most fur that is worn for clothing, which is the product of skinning by a hell-realm industry. So it's not just hell realms where hellish conditions exist; they exist here and now, where skinning alive is practiced in the leather and fur business. Removing the skin from dead animals is more difficult, so in many parts of the world, animals are skinned alive.[341] [342] [343][344] [345] Undercover investigators found that many animals struggled desperately when workers skinned them, and if this video is not a video of hell on earth I don't know what is.

peta.org/videos/a-shocking-look-inside-chinese-fur-farms/

What about the fish we eat? They are sentient and they suffer, too, as witnessed in this graphic video.

mercyforanimals.org/fish/

We smash their heads, we stack them on top of one another in the holds of ships, unable to move and breathe, out of the water, afraid and suffering, shivering on mounds of ice to keep them fresh for the market, slowly dying from suffocation and pressure from the thousands of bodies of their companions. This is so redolent of the cold hell realms.

We would never want to visit these places for one moment, let alone a lifetime, so why are we OK visiting this upon animals, directly or indirectly? Why is suffering OK for animals and not us? What is our karma for doing this to the animals? I personally cringe in pain when I make the temperature in the shower a little too hot, let alone the thought of being dipped in boiling water like that of a hot hell or slaughterhouse. I don't want to imagine being thrown on ice in the middle of 100,000 human beings in the hold of a huge ship.

Buddhists are animal lovers. I haven't met many who do not have animals as pets or have an affinity for animals. We save spiders and bees at retreats, gently capturing them and taking them outside so they will not accidentally get stepped on or sat upon. If we take the Bodhisattva vows, we vow to help all beings achieve freedom from suffering, and enlightenment. If hell realms exist, we vow freeing all in those dominions, too, even if we must go there. But when we transpose this goal and vow to help all sentient beings with the continued support of torture, confinement, and murder based on eating animals, disregarding what is on our plates and going into our mouths, what does that say about us? What is the karma created and what happens to Buddhists who disregard their own actions, their own karma in this activity? Whether unknowing or knowing participation, we still have a karmic debt to pay. As Buddhists, is it OK to just sit back; eat meat, fish, dairy, and eggs; and view this activity with passive dormancy, idly continuing to ingest our so-called comfort food? How do we sleep at night knowing that we are participants in creating hell realms on earth? How do we truly find a peaceful, truthful, grounded place to sit with ourselves, knowing we create hell realms for the animals we all say we love?

Carnage of cataclysmic proportions is happening each and every moment. It is a holocaust for animals where we torture, rape, and kill billions of beings beyond our personal ability to count and imagine. Approximately 70 billion land animals are confined and slaughtered annually, prompting author Charles Patterson to describe this as the *Eternal Treblinka* in his book of that name.[346]

The Buddha is often quoted in the Dharmapada, as saying,

> One who, while himself seeking happiness, oppresses with violence other beings who also desire happiness, will not attain happiness hereafter. One who, while himself seeking happiness, does not oppress with violence other

beings who also desire happiness, will find happiness hereafter.[347]

The animal realm is not considered a hell realm traditionally, but I strongly believe we have created one with our fascination for the taste of flesh, numb denial, and complacency to structural violence. Sawing, carving, slicing into pieces, burning, boiling, mashing, pounding, gouging, ripping, digging, disemboweling, skinning, severing, and dismembering are all functions of slaughter and vivisection. They are the same words used to describe life in hell realms. Whether it is an animal we subjugate and enslave for food, raise for fur, or test for drugs and cosmetics—or a human being reincarnated in a hell realm—the terminology and activity is the same. Why, if there are hell realms, should we be afforded this privilege? Why do we not think this will be our karma? How can we be so arrogant to think we will not reap what we sow when we are part of the market for tortured body parts in the form of meat, fish, dairy, eggs, drugs, clothing, and cosmetics?

Do we get a pass on this by saying "I didn't know"? Do we get a pass on this by saying "I really didn't delve into my action or inaction; I just did what everyone else did"? Do we get a pass because it's written by some monk(s), somewhere in Buddhist canon, that the Buddha said it was OK to eat meat if it met the deceiving three purity rules? In Jivaka Sutta from the Pali Canon, the source of the infamous three purity rules argument it is stated: "I say that there are three instances in which meat should not be eaten: when it is seen, heard, or suspected. I say that meat should not be eaten in those three instances."

These rules, when compared to the Buddha's teachings on compassion and especially the First Precept of doing no harm and respecting all life, seem deceptive. As Tashi Nyima states:

> Clearly, the Buddha is stipulating here that if a monk inadvertently consumes meat that has been placed in his begging bowl, he is not at fault. His action is pure. However, if he sees, hears, or even suspects that there is animal flesh in his bowl, he must not eat it.

> Later commentators gratuitously inserted the phrase "that the living being has been slaughtered for oneself" after each repetition of the word "suspected." The phrase does not appear in original the Pali text. It is a spurious addition, making it seem as if the Buddha allowed his monks to eat meat when the animal was not expressly killed to feed them, or at least when they did not see, hear, or suspect it.

> This interpolation is linguistically unwarranted. More importantly, it contradicts the unequivocal teaching of the Buddha on the matter. The Buddha gives extensive arguments against meat-eating in the Angulimaliya Sutra, Nirvana Sutra, Karma Sutra, Shurangama Sutra, Mahamegha Sutra, Lankavatara Sutra, Maha Parinirvana Sutra, and others.[348]

And even if we don't eat meat, fish, dairy, and eggs anymore, even if we don't wear leather or fur or use cosmetics tested on animals, is it the Buddhist path to remain passive and inactive in the face of suffering beings? What does the heroic archetype of the Bodhisattva inform us to do? Or has the Bodhisattva ideal become a meme passed on by our secular Buddhist culture like so many on social media, a humorous image, video, or piece of text, ineffective in contemporaneous action that helps other beings and ourselves?

In the Lankavatara Sutra it is said,

For the sake of profit, animals are killed, and wealth is given in exchange for meat. Slayer and buyer, both are caught in sin, and both will boil in hells of lamentation. All those who contravene the Buddha's word, who with an evil attitude partake of meat, destroy their lives, both now and those to come, and blight the discipline of Shakyamuni. [349]

In the Sutra of Close Mindfulness it is stated,

The denizens of hell will try to escape, but the hounds of hell will overtake and devour them whole: sinews and flesh, joint and bone, leaving nothing, not even a fragment the size of a mustard seed! Body and limbs will be completely eaten up. And this experience of being devoured by dogs will occur again and again. All this is said to be the result of killing living beings for the sake of enjoying their meat. [350]

Milarepa said,

Harmless beasts you slay and eat; you make and taste a drink to make you drunk and lay the cause for the Reviving Hell. Oh, do not jump into the gulf with open eyes. Take care, you gods and humankind, take care! When pricked by thorns, you cannot bear the pain, and yet you kill and eat the flesh of living beings. How harsh will be the prickle of Reviving Hell, when skin will be flayed from your burning limbs! So take away your dreadful blood-red meat. Here it is, unspoiled and quite untouched: take it now and use it as you wish![351]

I don't know if hell realms exist or not. And I am not buying or selling here. The First Law of Thermodynamics seems pretty clear that energy is neither created nor destroyed, just transformed. I do believe we go on in some capacity and are not just gone to sleep forever. Our minds are powerful and can create states of suffering or bliss. Whatever the case may be, I would rather end up on my deathbed an ethical vegan who changed his life and tried to create less suffering in the world, taking an active rather than passive role.

Buddhism is an active response to life through analysis, meditation, change of self, and social responsibility, which involves care and compassion for all sentient beings. If hell realms exist, it would seem that if we don't want to end up there with our bodies being cooked like peas in the Uncontrollable Torrent, we should in this life stop cooking the bodies of other sentient beings. We should adopt a compassionate vegan diet and lifestyle, ending the abuse of animals as much as possible within out control.

Hell Realms on Earth Not Mentioned in Buddhist Teachings

Being a Daughter and Mother Pig on a Factory Farm

My earliest memory is the fondest. I am playing with my brothers and sisters. Mom is lying on her side and we are feeding. We wonder why she is not getting up but we feed, call to her, play with each other, and sleep.

When I got a little older I was moved to a place where there were more of my kind, lots of cousins. It was very crowded, and then one day a man came over and led me away to a place where I was forcibly raped. I cried when they stuck things in my body and held me so that I could not run away. Later, my belly filled with my children and they were all born. I was confined the way my mother was, in a crate without being able to take care of my babies. I wanted to move but I could not. I wanted a better home. I wanted to go outside but I could not. I didn't want to soil myself by going to the bathroom where we all lived. I wanted to clean them, to nurture them, to show them how much I loved them, but all I could do was let them feed; this at least made me happy. I cried when I named them all. They learned their names very quickly. My children are so smart. I was sad when the men took them away. I was so very depressed. I cried. They came and raped me again. And again. And again.

Some time has passed and I have had many children. I never get to be near them for long; they are always taken from me too soon. They are taking me out of my cage. Are they going to rape me again? I am put on a truck. After a long ride we stop and are pushed out of the truck. I cannot walk. I am being beaten. I am walking. They corner me. They chain my legs. They cut my throat. I do not want to die and I fight them, bite at them, wheeze, and struggle with every ounce of energy as the lights dim and sounds fade.

Being a son on a Pig Factory Farm

I remember my mom, brothers, and sisters. Then I was confined in a crate. I don't know why. I want to run and go outside. I want fresh air and sun. I can't turn around and I have to pee so badly. I am peeing on the floor and it's getting on me. This is gross. I have to poop, I am pooping on the ground and I am stepping in it. I cannot get out of this cage. I bite the metal to free myself. I want to run and go outside. I want fresh air and sun. I want my mother and my sisters and brothers. I can hear my brothers calling me—they are here too. I call back. This cage is driving me crazy. I can hear my cell mates, I know them by name. We speak to one another when "they" are not around. I want to run and go outside. I want fresh air and sun. My legs are getting so tired. I can hardly stand up anymore. I don't know what they feed me but I am bigger now. My ankles hurt, my joints ache. I want to run and go outside. I want fresh air and sun.

They are taking me out! I am so happy, I smell fresh air. We are all being led onto a truck, a large metal truck. Everyone is crying. They are forcing more of us than can fit. It's too tight in here. I am next to the wall; my nose can smell the fresh air. It smells so good, but it's cold in here. The truck is moving. It is so painful, my body just aches. We are all crying out. My stomach is giving way; my intestines are coming out of my body. I don't want to die. I want to live. We are still on the road, it has been hours. It is so cold, I can no longer feel the side of my body against the metal. I want to run and go outside. I want warmth. We are slowing down. They are getting us out. I cannot move. I am stuck. I am yelling to brothers and to my friends. They are gone. Men are coming with iron bars and knives. They are prying me off the side of this metal truck, they are cutting my body. It hurts so bad, I am screaming, screaming with so much pain. Why are they making me suffer? I am passing out. I want to run and go outside. I want fresh air and warm sun.

I am awake again, upside down. Everything is pain, but especially my feet, which are bound by a chain. A man with a knife is cutting me; he's cutting my neck. My blood is coming out, my neck hurts so bad, my body hurts so bad, I am afraid, I don't want to die, I am struggling with all I have left. I want to run and go outside. I want fresh air and warm sun... [352] [353] [354] [355]

Does Eating Meat Come From Ignorance?

> "[It's] ignorance that drives the entire process... which isn't just an inability to apprehend the truth but an active misapprehension of the status of oneself and all other objects—one's own mind or body, other people, and so forth. It is the conception or assumption that phenomena exist in a far more concrete way than they actually do. Based on this misapprehension of the status of persons and things, we are drawn into afflictive desire and hatred... Not knowing the real nature of phenomena, we are driven to generate desire for what we like and hatred for what we do not like and for what blocks our desires. These three—ignorance, desire, and hatred— are called the three poisons; they pervert out mental outlook."
>
> ~ Jeffrey Hopkins [356]

We see ourselves as separate from animals. We have a clear misapprehension. We see ourselves as smarter, more important, since we have the ability to catch, cage, and take their freedom. Because of the differences between humans' and animals' abilities, we feel we have the right to kill and eat them. It's really very simple and it stems from the inability to see reality as it exists. It stems from not seeing connections. Its foundation is based on the falsehood that we are independent, solid, and intrinsically separate. We do not see ourselves as interdependent organisms whose very nature is dependent-origination tying us inextricably to each and every other being no matter the species.

All Buddhists are taught this. Do we feel it? See it? Know it? Model our behavior on it?

We have a harder time eating humans because we see ourselves. We see the connection, the fact that we humans all suffer and have the same desires for freedom and happiness. We agree we have unalienable rights to life, liberty, and the pursuit of happiness. Somehow we are able to disconnect our compassion when it comes to animals, especially when it comes to food. Through our cultural acceptance of animals as food, a Klesha (negative mental state that clouds the mind, causing suffering) of the group thought, we follow along allowing ourselves to see pigs, chicken, cows, bulls, fish, dairy, and eggs as food. "It" is separate from us, "they" are separate from us, and thus we can eat "it." As children we learned this to be true, and we became steadily attached to eating meat. We found it to be tasty and pleasurable, and believed it to be needed for the health of our precious body. We found it as a way to connect with our families and their traditions; it gave us identity. Meat became part and parcel of who we are, and this attachment to the broiled, fried, baked, and boiled corpses of sentient beings comes from not seeing them as the same as us. They are different. They are them and we are us. This is misapprehension and ignorance of reality; intrinsically we are connected. Thich Naht Hahn calls this "Inter-are" and "Interbeing."

Formerly, as a meat-eating Buddhist I didn't really want to question this too deeply, because there would then have been a psychological rift, a cognitive dissonance. This would have caused me pain and suffering and would lead me to questioning what I had always done, what I had been raised to do. It would force me to see that eating meat is just like eating my child, my mother, my brother or sister. But isn't this the point of Dharma practice? To cause us some pain, make us look at ourselves, tear down our ego-centered ways?

Ringu Tulku states:

In the Buddhist sense, ignorance is equivalent to the identification of a self as being separate from everything else. It consists of the belief that there is an "I" that is not part of anything else. On this basis we think, "I am one and unique. Everything else is not me. It is something different."...

From this identification stems the dualistic view, since once there is an "I," there are also "others." Up to here is "me." The rest is "they." As soon as this split is made, it creates two opposite ways of reaction: "This is nice, I want it!" and "This is not nice, I do not want it!"[357]

So on the one hand, there are those things that seem to threaten or undermine us because maybe they will harm us or take away our identity or comfortable ways of living, and thus aversion rises. Then on the other hand, there are those things that are nice and we want them and thus attachment arises. One of our greatest attachments is to eating and using animal products. We like to wear them, sit in them, and eat them. But the reasons for eating meat and using animals, an exceedingly nihilistic behavior pattern in today's world, no longer apply. Might does not make right and is spelling out doom for the planet and our health, and nihilism is rejected by Buddhist teachings.

Eating Meat, Fish, Dairy, and Eggs Is Nihilistic

When there are hundreds of healthy plant-based choices but we continue to choose to eat the bodies of sentient beings, we are acting with nihilism. The very act of eating another being makes the statement: I don't think there is a future, and if there is I don't care. May it be damned. This strong statement is accurate on many levels. When we eat animals, we certainly don't care for our own life and health. We certainly don't care about the health of our world or its future. We certainly don't care for animals, since we consider they are "them" and we are "us." As such there is a fundamental belief in duality and separateness when we deem we have the right to kill them with impunity and eat them. We certainly don't care about future rebirth, if there is reincarnation, since killing is an unskillful act that creates great negativity. Unskillful deeds like killing devolve our karma; they do not evolve it. Therefore, eating meat is akin to the belief that when you die, that's it.

But while there is no proof that we go on after life, there is similarly no proof we do not. If we take a simple common sense approach to this, it becomes apparent we may want to err on the side of there being something that does go on after life and learn to live more compassionately.

If our aim is to build muscle, we go to the gymnasium and lift weights. If our aim is to better our memory, we play certain video or card games designed to help memorization. If we want better health, we eat a WFPB diet. Doing these things creates a common karma here and now: bigger muscles, better memory, and improved health. If something continues after our death, it follows that how you lived so will you be reborn. Our acts will either evolve us up the karmic ladder or devolve us down. Ethics are not thus arbitrary but tied to our actions here and now and in the future. Just as in life, if we live by the sword we die by the sword. This suggests we create more space to learn to care for others, as our acts shape our state of being—here and now and in the future.

The value in being ethical is caring for ourselves and others, which creates openness in our hearts. Killing ourselves and others creates a closed-ness and shutting down and armoring of ourselves. Killing eliminates space. When we are open-hearted we don't need Kevlar. But when we kill others, a Kevlar vest may be needed, since others are likely to do to us what we did to them. This is true even with the virtual Kevlar Wall of Carnism we create based on our need to separate ourselves from our true feelings and actions toward animals we arbitrarily consider food. Open hearts by definition have no boundary, but closed hearts do. You can find evidence of a closed heart if you look at your plate of food and see there is a sentient being's body or secretion there.

Are we here forever in some capacity or are we gone when we die? This question can be central to ethical actions. There are reasons to be kind if we do believe in reincarnation or if we don't.

If we do not believe in a continuum of life after death, then does it matter what we do as there may be no result we will meet? Yes. Negativity in this life is still followed by more negativity. There is still a karmic effect to unethical actions whether we believe in reincarnation or not. What we sow we shall reap.

If we believe we go on, we may want to act in ways that do not harm others, because when we consider the Heart Sutra which states matter is emptiness and emptiness is matter (supported by the equation $E=mc^2$ and the First Law of Thermodynamics) we have additional evidence that there may be some sort of continuation. Additionally, there is a multitude of anecdotal data collected and published over the years of people remembering past lives clearly. There is a strong case that life does not end with death, it only transforms. The most sensible approach to this is that we expect our experience to continue, just as when we go to sleep and wake, then being kind and acting ethically to others including animals considered food or used for entertainment and laboratory testing is a key benefit to us in the future for a positive reincarnation.

Transcendent wisdom means we transcend our self-centered ways of ignorance and delusion of separateness. The Buddha taught we can choose blissful lives connected to others or miserable lives disconnected. Remember the Buddha's universe right from the beginning consisted of all beings, *sabbe sattva.* Connections with all beings make us happy, and disconnection keeps us miserable. We make the choices for ourselves, and nothing can make you blissful except a fully open heart and transcendent wisdom, seeing ourselves and others as not separate. If you don't believe in reincarnation, this is the very reason and argument for being kind in this life. There is karma in this lifetime. If you want to experience happiness, then see the connection between us all, and do not kill or cause to kill. Have respect for all life.

Eating others keeps a part of us locked in self-centeredness. Seeing the connection between ourselves and others, the connectedness of our planet's systems of biological diversity, and the negative nature of "might makes right," we can then choose to transcend our self-centered ignorance and misapprehension. Eating meat, fish, dairy, and eggs is a fundamental misknowing for which we will not be given a karmic pass. As the planet warms, species go extinct, and the world becomes depleted, we will pay a price. If we believe we can eat meat, fish, dairy and eggs and get away with this negative behavior, we are deluded. Karma is definite. Karma is now. If we are the cause of greenhouse gases, the temperature will rise. The more we are a cause, the more it will rise. If we eat meat, fish, dairy, and eggs, we will get the associated diseases. We will also be the cause for beings to be killed on our behalf. This is unskillful action and behavior.

Unskillful action is the killing of life. This is the reason it is the first ethical precept in Buddhism and a law in most other spiritual paths. When we kill another being through purchasing its body parts in a container in a store, we are stating, "I don't identify with you and you don't own your body, I do!" It is truly a nihilistic action. But if we choose to not eat beings (meat, fish, dairy, and eggs), we are expanding our sense of connection to them. We care for them. Expansion of connection is relational; we see the relationality between us, and between global warming, species extinction, human health, and spiritual harmony. Extending our connections means we save more and more lives. When we kill, we narrow and our actions state we don't connect.

Is the spiritual path one of closing down and contracting or one of opening up our hearts and minds with expansion?

The Buddhist path is taught as an infinite, rather than finite, path, with infinite beings to help and have compassion for during our journey. During this long journey, we learn to embody generosity. Generosity is a form of expansion because we give ourselves to others. Generosity is the opposite of the second precept of stealing or taking something which is not given freely. Generosity is enthusiastic altruism where we expand our perceptions to include fish, lobsters, coral reefs, pelagic fish, pigs cows, steers, calves, chickens, roosters, turkeys, goats, sheep, and lambs, seeing in these animals their own right to happiness. When we connect with them we know we cannot steal their lives but should practice being generous and choose plant-based, environmentally sound foods. When we choose to eat plant-based food, we connect with these animals who are the receivers of our generosity. This is how a vegan lifestyle nurtures our health, spirit, and the planet in a gentle warm embrace.

The great Buddhist master Nagarjuna stated "Shunyata Karuna Garbham," (Sanskrit)[358] where:

- *Shunyata* means emptiness, voidness, or the total relationality and connectedness of all things
- *Karuna* means great compassion for all
- *Garbham* literally means the womb

What Nargarjuna was saying is that the entire interrelatedness of all phenomena and sentient beings are held in the loving womb embraced by compassion. Put differently, emptiness is the womb from which great compassion ascends. Ultimate happiness and bliss occurs when we break down all the barriers between us and them and connect with the relationality of all life. Seen in this light, emptiness is not nothingness but rather a gentle epidermis of total interjoining, bonding, and association. Living a vegan lifestyle helps us get there, as it signifies we see clearly the association between ourselves and others. We do not eat them, wear them, use products tested on them, or go to entertainment venues which use them. Vegans see the connection. Vegans expand the connection to include the earth and other humans. This is an apprehension of the truth of our total interrelatedness, our dependent origination, and *Shunyata Karuna Garbham.*

Eating meat, fish, dairy, and eggs shuts down empathy, compassion, and connections with other beings. It shuts down our association to the planet and our own awakening. It is a nihilistic action that states clearly I don't care. Not eating meat, fish, dairy, and eggs, and living a vegan lifestyle, on the other hand, actively shows through our behavior that we care, connect, and have compassion. A vegan lifestyle opens our hearts, it does not close them. Therefore, a vegan way of life can engender transcendent wisdom, eradication of nihilism, and the embracing of others.

Historical reasons for eating meat no longer apply

Everywhere you look in Buddhist philosophy, questions point us to ponder our reliance on animal foods. Our precious body is a vehicle to help us become awake. When we feed our bodies animal food, knowing we are increasing our risk factors for heart disease, stroke, diabetes, and many types of cancers, are we respecting it? Are we being compassionate when we know other beings suffer so greatly and don't want to die. Have we really incorporated the understanding of emptiness, shunyata, and dependent origination when we can easily eat a steak without feeling connected to the being who unwillingly gave its life for the food? Can we say we are following a compassionate lifestyle when we add to the destruction of our oceans, land, and climate? Do we feel generous or happy to be an additional cause of the sixth great extinction? Is it wise to be a factor in global depletion and continued injustice to slaughterhouse workers and their families, as well as our own communities? While it is our mental habituation and karma that keeps us from seeing this clearly, can't we do something about it?

Historically, because we needed to survive, we had to eat animals from time to time. Eating animals to survive turned into a custom, and the human species has built up thousands of years of excuses to support the habit— Buddhists included. Did awakened masters see the negativity? Yes. But perhaps they reasoned, why make people feel bad about what they were doing to survive? For much of human history it was perhaps necessary for survival. If it was necessary, what was a teacher with great compassion to do? Lay useless guilt upon their followers? Feeling guilty for what you are doing to animals doesn't help when you are in a survival mode, without the availability of plants to eat. As far as I know, the Buddha did not teach guilt as a positive trait. So one can understand why historically a Buddhist monk, master, and teacher would not do that.

But that was yesteryear. The case today is that plant food is abundant. Especially when you live in India, Western Europe, Canada, Asia, or the United States, where plant foods are plentiful, there is no need to hold onto this old conditioning, this pervasive suffering to which we are indoctrinated and accustomed. Even in places considered to be scarce of plant food, if plant food was not fed to animals or sold to be fed to animals elsewhere, there would be much more food available for people.

Awakening to the very important point in the Buddha's teaching on the first two Noble Truths is key: Suffering exists and there is a cause to suffering. The cause, as discussed, is that we separate ourselves from our fellow earthlings, animals and humans. Perhaps for reasons of survival, we learned to shut down and turn away, but this is not necessary now. We no longer need to separate ourselves from the animals caught up in the identical samsaric struggle as we are; we should put ourselves in their places. If we don't gaze from their point of view, we will continue to live under this conditioning, this false belief that keeping them as prisoners, slaughtering them, and eating their flesh is somehow good for us. Eating others is not good for us physically, mentally, and spiritually. We don't need to eat meat, fish, dairy, and eggs. It is time to stop.

How could I pray in the morning for all sentient beings' freedom and eat them at lunch?

In the sky, there is no distinction of east and west. People create distinctions out of their own minds and then believe them to be true.

The Buddha

Shortly after becoming vegan, I looked back and wondered how a person who was actively trying to awaken himself could have prayed for the end of suffering for all sentient beings, sit on a cushion, and meditate on the Four Immeasurables (below) in the morning, and then eat a chicken for lunch?

> May all beings have happiness
> May they be free from suffering
> May they find the joy that has never known suffering
> May they be free from attachment and hatred

Prior to becoming an ethical vegan, I considered myself a compassionate person; I have never knowingly wished to hurt anyone in any grave manner. I did not hunt, fish, or kill anything intentionally. I captured unwanted suffering spiders, hornets, bees, and ants in the house in the summer, and gently released them outdoors, unharmed. I got very upset when I once hit and killed a raccoon when it was running across the road at night and I was unable unable to stop my car in time. I was appalled after many years of practice to see fish being caught by fisherman, watching the fish gasp for air and die, suffering and struggling. I was appalled and yet able to go to the local restaurant on Friday evening and order the "all you can eat" fish and chips dinner. What was it that allowed me to act this way? To act completely unconsciously? Something was shut down in me. What was it?

One clear answer to my question is found in the work of Melanie Joy, PhD, in her book entitled _Why We Love Dogs, Eat Pigs and Wear Cows_. Dr. Joy defines a new term, "carnism," and describes quite well what was going on with me when I sat down at the table and my compassion went blind.

According to Dr. Joy, "carnism is the invisible belief system, or ideology, that conditions people to eat certain animals. Carnism is essentially the opposite of veganism; "carn" means "flesh" or "of the flesh" and "ism" denotes a belief system. Most people view eating animals as a given, rather than a choice; in meat-eating cultures around the world people typically don't think about why they find the flesh of some animals disgusting and the flesh of other animals appetizing, or why they eat any animals at all. But when eating animals is not a necessity for survival, as is the case in much of the world today, it is a choice—and choices always stem from beliefs." [359] This is the definition that starts to get to the root cause of our ignorance around this issue.

She goes on to describe how a carnist belief system works and how it blocks and interrupts our consciousness. I realized by reading Dr. Joy's book that what I thought I was doing, practicing free will, when I had been eating meat was certainly not the case. I had been an unconscious automaton, not a conscious meditator choosing what he wished to eat. I had been a willing participant in violent ideology without even knowing it. I was a willing participant in the herding culture structural system of violence 10,000 years old.[360]

Dr. Joy posits a scenario at the beginning of her book of a dinner party. It is a beautiful scene with a pleasant table setting, candle lit with fragment aromas parading the room arousing taste buds. Hunger pains from not eating all day arise while the host brings out a wonderful meat stew with veggies and gravy. The guests help themselves and find the food delicious, and after a few mouthfuls they ask for her recipe which the host begins to explain, a little olive oil, a little mirepoix, some vegetables and "5 pounds of golden retriever, well marinated." Imagine all chewing stops. Freeze frame. All realize they have golden retriever in their mouths and with consciousness now fully awake, revulsion sets in. What tasted fantastic a few seconds ago now is revolting. They can't swallow, or chew anymore, and they don't want to be rude and spit the mouthful into their napkins.

What just happened, Dr. Joy posits. The food did not change. It tasted great one moment and then repulsive. What occurred is we ran into the brick wall of our own mental schema, or our culture's way of looking at what is OK to eat and what is not OK to eat. Beef is OK. Dog is not OK. The perception we have for dogs in the U.S. is different than in many parts of the world and so our feelings are different. A Korean, Vietnamese, or Chinese person may not have stopped eating at all. But as Dr. Joy—and the Buddha—taught perceptions define our vision of reality. We perceive it's OK to eat beef but not OK to eat dog. Dogs are our companions; we speak, play, share our homes, and care for them. They speak to us, teach us, and share their lives with us. We feed, groom, and nurse them when they are sick. We don't eat dogs for the same reason we don't eat humans: We have kinship with them, see them with a perception that is close. We love our dogs. They are family members. They are us, not them. In Buddha's terminology, we don't have "aversion" or even feelings of neutrality to them in the U.S. but an affinity, a pleasant feeling. They make us happy, and we like pleasure (we are attracted/attached).

Dr. Joy discusses our schema, the way we see the world, noting that "our perceptions are due to our schema." Furthermore she writes, "A schema is a psychological framework that shapes—and is shaped by—our beliefs, ideas, perceptions, and experiences, and it automatically organizes and interprets incoming information." [361] Accordingly we have a schema for everything, every vegetable, each different race, all the different species of animals, and which animals we consider as food, clothing, and friends. This is exactly the type of schema ancient Buddhist meditation practices such as 7-point Mind Training, Lojong, Generating Loving Kindness, Creating Bodhichitta, Tonglen (giving and taking), and Exchanging Self and Others are designed to illuminate and eradicate.[362] [363]

Dr. Joy goes on to say, "And something interesting happens when we are confronted with the meat from an animal we've classified as inedible: We automatically picture the living animal from which it came, and we tend to feel disgusted at the notion of eating it. The perceptual process follows this sequence:

Golden retriever meat (stimulus) > inedible animal (belief/perception) > image of living dog (thought) > disgust (feeling) > refusal or reluctance to eat (action)"

This model fits exactly what has happened to me when I became vegan. When I started to teach myself all about where animal food comes from, I began to visualize the animals. This visualization was based on my changed belief and perceptions through the education and my self-imposed diet change, via the 30-day vegan challenge. I began to see the animals in front of me on the plate. Eggs are one good example of what I see now.

Eggs (stimulus) > sentient being with feelings who suffers (belief/perception) > image a chicken in a factory farm in a cage, image of males chicks being sorted from the females and ground up alive, image of the female chicks having their beaks cut off (thought) > disgust (feeling) > refusal to eat (action)

I do this routinely now. I try at every meal to be mindful and present to what it is I am eating, where it came from, that it did not suffer and that it is natural and healthy for my body. It is a function of rejoicing in the positive nature of eating a plant-based diet. But it is difficult when sharing a table with meat eaters, when I glance at their food. I see suffering beings on their plates.

As Dr. Joy explains, most people who sit at the dining room table do not envision the animal from which the meat on their plate originated, they just see food. We eat and skip thinking about where it comes from; we go blind. Why is it we go blind when we sit down at the table to eat? The answer seems to lie with the concept of psychic numbing, a process of disconnecting mentally, emotionally, and probably spiritually, too. Psychic numbing is dualistic in nature, having positive attributes when it helps us cope with violence, and negative when it allows us to enable violence (like the violence that occurs in factory farming CAFOs, slaughterhouses, and on our plates).

Psychic numbing is made up of a complex array of defenses and other mechanisms, mechanisms which are pervasive, powerful, and invisible and which operate on both social and psychological levels. These mechanisms distort our perceptions and distance us from our feelings, transforming our empathy into apathy—indeed, it is the process of learning to not feel that is the focus of this book. The mechanisms of psychic numbing include: denial, avoidance, routinization, justification, objectification, deindividualization, dichotomization, rationalization, and dissociation. [364]

It is quite interesting to hear this from Dr. Joy, when as a Buddhist practitioner these are all the very same mechanisms we are trying to make visible, feel, and overcome (even if only for temporary moments). We strive to realize these unconscious mechanisms and free ourselves from them. We attempt to realize our denial and avoidance in being present for ourselves, loved ones, and all sentient beings. We try not to live in denial but see the truth of our conditions, our situation, and our life in order to make needed changes. Unless we are awakened to our own issues, unless we are pointing the finger back at our own negativity, what improvement can be made? But when we pray, meditate, read, and converse on topics of compassion, peace, and freedom and then go eat a steak sandwich, we reinforce the very behaviors we seek to eradicate. Eating meat, dairy, and eggs keeps these mechanisms in place and is in direct opposition to awakening our mind and heart. Justifying what we do only adds to our denial. Objectifying others leads us further into believing our dualistic perceptions of us and them, on all levels of our lives, not just eating meat.

Dissociation from others is not what we strive for, but rather we endeavor to develop association with others.

Can we be engaged and dissociated? How can we be connected to others when in disconnected denial, caught in our meat-eating routines with a justified objectification of individuals who we de-individualize, dissociate from, and rationalize as other? Seen in this light, how could eating meat ever be part of the Buddhist path or any spiritual path? How could a Bodhisattva, who is dedicated to having ultimate compassion and empathy, ever participate in this action? Perhaps this is why so many great masters from the past were vegetarians and vegans, including Buddha Shakyamuni, Atisha, Milarepa, Drikung Kyobpa, Taklung Thangpa, Phagmo Drupa, Thogme Zangpo, Drukpa Kunleg, Jigme Lingpa, Nyakla Pema Dudul, Shabkar, Khendrup Je, Pratrul Rinpoche, and Kyabje Pabongka Rinpoche.

> In the case of Patrul Rinpoche, the celebrated author of *The Words of My Perfect Teacher,* it is well known that, through his incessant exposition of the Bodhicharyavatara and his represented teachings on the helpless plight of animals, he effectively abolished, in many parts of Tibet, the practice of slaughtering animals and offering their meat to visiting lamas. [365]

We Stop Feeling and Thinking

> *We manage to swallow flesh only because we do not think of the cruel and sinful thing that we do.*

> Rabindranath Tagore

We do not think. Tagore puts carnism in simple terms. We do not think when we eat meat. We stop thinking, analyzing, feeling, and having empathy, compassion, and love. We become unconscious when we eat. We make the act of eating meat invisible. Indeed, invisibility is the principal defense of our mind, which keeps the system of eating meat in existence. Without invisibility we lose our insulation; we begin to see the animal for what they are, we see the raising and slaughter and we begin to expose the system.

This is in direct opposition to what a Buddhist practitioner does (or is supposed to do). A practitioner creates visibility, honors the true nature of things, and does not want to have invisible states of consciousness. The first, second, and fourth Noble Truths are about making the invisible visible; a Bodhisattva creates visibility in their mind. They do the opposite of what society and culture has taught them in some cases. They make schema visible and then negate it, refute it, and come out the cocoon of denial with a clear mind. Buddhist practitioners attempt to break down their schemas through meditative absorption and complete questioning of our ideas, perceptions, and experiences whose goal is greater compassion, revealing and stopping the violence in our lives and the lives of others. Denial does not help us change. This is a place where Buddhism and science can merge, where research, exploration, meditation, and finding the truth come together.

Invisibly Present Carnism

When I look back today at all the retreats, teachings, seminars, initiations, empowerments, podcasts, and other dharma events I have attended, I realize there was and is a dearth of information yet no discussion about the effect of eating animals on one's spiritual path. It's missing. It's not part of the teachings. It's not in books, meditations, prayers, or discussions. It is as invisible as the slaughterhouses and the 70 billion land animals slaughtered in them, while we all drive in our cars and trucks, seeing humans traveling everywhere but never seeing the billions of animals being raised and killed in our midst.

Billions of land animals being raised in our midst yet they are obscured. We see only a scant portion from time to time, here and now, on an old-style throwback farm, but not the billions upon billions we raise. And just like every grocery store whose counters are continually stocked with the body parts of sentient beings, the information is there, ignored by almost all teachers and students ubiquitously. The effects of our human habit of eating meat are missing from our personal schema and the Western delivery of dharma teachings in countless many cases. Carnism runs deep in the West and it runs deep in the new Western Buddhism. A few phone calls to Dharma centers in the U.S. Midwest uncover an alarming trend no matter the lineage. Most centers are not vegetarian, let alone vegan, and 90% support the eating of meat on their premises all while teaching compassion for all sentient beings.

Pointing the finger back at myself, the discussion of meat eating was right in front of me all the time but veiled. It was acknowledged with each reference to suffering, freedom, and the path as it points toward all sentient life. But when I was a meat eater with my carnist goggles on, I only referenced compassion for humans. The change in my diet afforded me the opportunity to look deeper and see what was always there. Explicitly, the dharma, as taught in the West, is not focused on animals. There is perhaps a twofold reason for this:

- Teachers who want to continue eating meat, whose responsibility it is to help us identify the oil in the stained cloth of our own Buddha-nature, can in a self-serving way skip over this issue.
- The taboo nature of the subject, since it goes against the norms of our society and the agricultural-pharmaceutical-medical-governmental-military-educational-religious complex.

Looking back on my early years in Buddhism, I wonder if it would have turned me off to hear clearly the message of veganism as part of the teachings? Would it have pushed me away had it been discussed after I had become a committed practitioner? It is often stated that Buddhism has infiltrated many societies, in its 2,600-year history, through full assimilation of the customs and traditions of the new culture. Is this something that was needed before Buddhism could be accepted in the West? Or am I only now seeing this as I am a vegan and my paradigm has shifted?

In the West, this is an undoubtedly uncomfortable topic to bring up, very difficult to broach, unquestionably taboo. But confront it we must. It is a necessary topic to explore. Just as the Buddha did not shy away from bringing the untouchable caste into the sangha and treating them like everyone else, he also taught that killing was violence and that eating meat was the outcome of violence. Buddha identified structural violence in his society and taught the path to uncover our internal complicity with such systems.

In my attempt to be an ethical vegan and Buddhist practitioner, today I see the vegan message in the Lam Rim, the Bodhisattva's Way of Life, the Lama Chopa, Heart Sutra, the Seven Limb practice, Lojong, Tonglen, in subtle teachings of Ganden Lha Gyema, Three Principles of the Path, Vajrayogini, Tara, Heruka, Yamantaka, Gujasamaja, Manjushri, Avelokitesvara, and in basically all sutra and tantra teaching which pervade all three Buddhist vehicles (Theravada, Mahayana, Vajrayana). The fact is eating meat is against the teachings of the Buddha from every level of practice and discipline, and the fact that I and others never wanted (nor want) to see it, speaks to our own carnist perspectives. Now that I do not eat meat, fish, dairy, and eggs, I see the message clearly.

The Buddha was aware of the schema on eating meat. He knew it was an imperceptible killer of compassion, so on his death bed he taught, as documented in the Lankavatara sutra, that "For innumerable reasons, Mahamati, the Bodhisattva, whose nature is compassion, is not to eat any animal flesh... For a Bodhisattva to keep good integrity with the Dharma, he or she should not make any exceptions to the eating of animal flesh."[366]

Negativity Creates positivity?

Let him not destroy, or cause to be destroyed, any life at all, or sanction the acts of those who do so. Let him refrain even from hurting any creature, both those that are strong and those that tremble in the world.

The Buddha, Dhammika Sutta

When we believe that meat eating is a biological imperative, necessary for survival, then killing is necessary. It is easy to take the next logical step to rationalize killing as something that serves the greater good; it is required for humans to live and thrive. And as a human rebirth is a precious commodity in the Buddhist cosmology, because we can become awake and become a Buddha, the killing of animals when believed necessary for humans can be seen as creating positivity. Subsequently, we explain to ourselves that it's an attribute of samsara, a terrible game played on us by this realm we live in. In order for us to live, food animals (chickens, pigs, cows, sheep, lambs, and fish) must die. However, as we know, this is not the case. It is a human construct. It is without merit and hidden from view under layers of upbringing, culture, tradition, and taste. Just wanting to believe something (due to culture, upbringing, and endless commercials) does not make it so. We recognize karma doesn't work in this fashion; we know we cannot create positive results with a negative action.

The Buddha taught that positivity creates positivity and negativity creates negativity. Our own positive or negative thoughts, emotions, motivations, and actions create what we will experience in the future. Coming from a belief in reincarnation, this can occur either in this life or future lives. If it occurs in this life it has been called "common result" or "instant Karma." Karma has many attributes, but primarily it is considered: A) definite because if your action is negative it will manifest in a negative result, and if your action is positive it will manifest a positive result; B) it is fast growing because it can multiply and compound upon itself; and C) you are bound to meet the result whether it is good or bad if you created it (conversely, you will not meet a result you did not create). Karma is something we create by ourselves, and everything we experience comes from our own karma; the comedy and tragedy of our lives is based on our own distinct karma.

Choosing to be unaware of something doesn't nullify its negativity. Killing, we know, is negative. We know instinctively that animals suffer, because we are empathic beings and we suffer. We know animals want life and will strive to do anything to live up until the moment their hearts stop beating. Our disregarding of their suffering in factory farms and in slaughterhouses, due to the fact we wish to eat them and pay someone else to kill them does not invalidate our negative karma. Our carnist imperceptible belief system does not create positivity when it overrides the teachings on compassion and what we know in our hearts. Our denial of addiction to meat, fish, dairy, and eggs does not nullify our responsibility and accountability to other beings, our own health, and the well-being of the planet but becomes a shelter for negative thoughts and behaviors to grow. Denial is a dark harbor for undesirable beliefs and activities.

The Buddha was aware of the carnist schema, as have been many great masters. In the Lankavatara Sutra, he taught that killing and thus eating of meat was against the path of awakening and extinguished the seed of compassion. He knew it interrupted and blocked our ability to become awake.

Eating fish, beef, pork, chicken, dairy, and eggs—or eating any animal product ,all the while trying to be compassionate within other areas of life—is a form of repression. I have been guilty of this. It is how I and all other compassionate people, Buddhists and non-Buddhists alike, are capable of eating meat, fish, dairy, and eggs. We repress the truth. We are not awake to what is, to the reality of the situation, and our consciousness thus blocked allows for negative action. We become entrapped by the invisible schema named carnism, and while we believe we have compassion, it is very limited compassion, if any at all.

The Buddha taught that the path of awakening ourselves to all our schemas was through ethical behavior encapsulated by meditation, generosity, patience, enthusiasm, concentration, and wisdom. The enlightening path is one where all things are exposed, all cultural baggage is identified, and all the negativities of ego, body, and mind are eliminated through compassionate application of ethical methods. He taught it was our job to train our mind, to calm it so that we could see with greater clarity. And with that clarity we could overcome our defilements of the mind to find out who we truly are, to awaken our hearts. In other words, our work is to identify, understand, and eliminate all schemas that keep us ignorant, blocked and in a state of repression. It is our job to make a direct association between the training of our minds toward ultimate love and compassion for all beings. This is the way of the Bodhisattva who sees no difference between animals and loved ones. It is our job to train our mind and perfect our mental capacity to see no separation from animals (all beings) and our self. And thus Lama Shabkar Tsogdruk Rangdrol, wrote:

> When these mental disciplines have been perfected—when, for instance, one has a vivid sense that all beings have been as kind and close to us as our own dear parents—it becomes literally impossible to feed upon their flesh. By contrast, the taking of meat, regarded as an ordinary food and eaten unreflectively on a regular basis, implies an unawareness and an indifference to the suffering of beings that is incompatible with the mind training.[367]

When we eat meat, fish, dairy, and eggs without thought of the consequences, we act as though a negative action will bear a positive result. But all the while, the common result of this karma is clear for us to see. Logical investigation would strongly suggest we are deluded. The fact is that we cannot hide from this hushed, played down, unmindful karmic result as it is written about daily, talked about daily, and experienced daily in our lives. We cannot turn on a television set without seeing an advertisement for a drug that will help with diabetes, cancer, heart disease, stroke, or erectile dysfunction. While it is not my job to make sweeping pronouncements about karma in this writing, I will leave it to your judgment as to whether there is truth here worth understanding at a deeper level. It has become clear that when we kill an animal and eat its flesh, we become afflicted with the many diseases associated with affluence and the Western diet. These diseases are rampant in "modern society," whose diets are based upon meat. This business of eating animals also threatens us all collectively with global environmental collapse of all ecosystems on land, sea, and air, as 30% to 50% of global warming origins is caused by our addiction to eating meat, fish, dairy, and eggs. This collapse presages the very survival of humans as a species. And so when we enslave, slaughter, and eat 70 billion land animals and 1 trillion sea animals each and every year, is it not plausible that we will then be killed? Is it not plausible that what we sow we shall reap? When we as a human species act without humanity and murder 133,000 land animals per minute and 1.8 million sea creatures per minute, every day, is there no karmic result? Is not the destruction of our health and the well-being of the entire planet not in some sense the outcome of a common result, an instant karma, both for the individual and collective?

Karma and Reincarnation

> *At the time of death our positive karma will help and our negative karma will harm... How you lead your life, where you've been will tell you where you are going.*
>
> ~ Gelek Rimpoche, 2/16/2014,
> Mahamudra Teachings, Ann Arbor, Mi.

The idea there is something beyond this life is a standard and accepted concept in Buddhism, as in most other religions. Whether there is something that goes on after this life is a debatable subject. But if we suspend judgment for a moment and accept this as true, how does this speak to whether we are ethical vegans or eaters of meat, fish, dairy, and eggs?

Knowing what we know about the negative attributes of eating meat, that an animal must be born in complete captivity as a prisoner, suffer in that captivity, be fed an unnatural diet, and then be forcibly pushed down pathways into the slaughterhouse, down the killing chutes to its death—we recognize this is destructive. Knowing as we do that no beings want to die and all beings suffer, then we know that eating meat is very negative because it causes suffering and death. When we consider its effects on our health and that we help to promote various diseases by eating of meat, fish, dairy, and eggs, we realize we are harming our body and causing a premature debilitation. We come to find our bodies are hurt due to our habits and taste. Another negativity. When we consider the high amounts of pollution to the air, water, and land caused by eating meat, we realize the negative effects we have on the planet, the mother of all life as we know it. This earth, our only planet, suffers and is dying due to our habits and tastes. When we add up all these negativities and we take the statement of Gelek Rimpoche's (that there is such a thing as karma and that we can be reborn) as true, how can we continue to eat meat, fish, dairy, and eggs?

If you would rather lead the rest of your life with more positivity, which leads to a virtuous afterlife (if there is an afterlife), then choosing a vegan diet is the prudent thing to do. If you would like to lead your life with more negativity from killing animals, your body, and the earth, then by all means continue with the habit of eating meat, fish, dairy, and eggs. Where you end up is up to you based on what you do, the effort you put in, the things you have learned and implemented in your life. A vegan friend once said, "Not eating sweets and sugary foods takes discipline, but being vegan takes values." What do you value? Where are your values? What are you willing to change to bring about change for yourself, the planet, and all sentient life on earth? And where will your choice take you after you die, if there is such a thing as reincarnation? Will your life's actions cause you to be in a better or worse condition? Will you evolve up or down? And even if there is no such thing as life after death, heaven, hell, or a continuation of any sort, do we wish to leave a dead and depleted planet to those generations who will follow? How can any reasonable person believe negativity will lead to positivity?

The World Is Burning

In the Addittapariyaya Sutta/Sutra, The Fire Sermon, we find the "Discourse on the Way of Expressing Phenomena as Being on Fire" or the so-called fire metaphor. The Buddha taught a number of mendicants in Gaya who were fire worshippers, it is said. It's recorded that he instructed these fire-worshiping ascetics on the foundation of all suffering based on craving (attachment), hatred (aversion), and delusion (ignorance). This ancient teaching is just as appropriate for today's world as it was 2,500 years ago. It deserves our full attention and contemplation. It is written the Buddha said:

> Bhikkus, all the world is burning. And what is burning?
>
> The eye is burning, visible forms are burning, visual consciousness is burning... Burning with what? Burning with the fire of craving, with the fire of hate, with the fire of delusion...
>
> The nose is burning, odors are burning, olfactory consciousness is burning... Burning with what? Burning with the fire of craving, with the fire of hate, with the fire of delusion...
>
> The tongue is burning, flavors are burning, gustative consciousness is burning... Burning with what? Burning with the fire of craving, with the fire of hate, with the fire of delusion...
>
> The body is burning, tangible things are burning, tactile consciousness is burning... Burning with what? Burning with the fire of craving, with the fire of hate, with the fire of delusion...

> The mind is burning, mental objects [ideas and concepts] are burning, mental consciousness is burning... Burning with what? Burning with the fire of craving, with the fire of hate, with the fire of delusion...

Stephen Batchelor believes the fire metaphor is very suited to describe what is happening to the environment today.[368] I agree and take it a couple steps further, as I believe there isn't a more apropos teaching for today's dilemma from a health, environmental, and animal rights context.

The world is plainly getting hotter. We have the ability to quantify it and according to NASA we were 1.5 degrees Celsius hotter in 2016 than ever previously recorded.[369 370 371] We are literally, not just metaphorically, getting warmer. And according to the Buddha, this is caused by craving, hate, and delusion, the three poisons. And as fire devours any object, or consumes any object, we literally are consumers in a circle of craving, hate, and delusion, inside of a global community of consumerism. We are driven to consume. We are the fire and we have a sense that consuming is happiness and will solve our problems, driven by marketing, television, and the corporate global economy. We are quite literally a world driven by consumerism for meat, fish, dairy, and eggs, along with all the other products we consume (Apple phones, clothes, entertainment, transportation) that destroy the entire world. While it is easy to see that hatred drives the conflicts and wars around the world, it is harder to see the connection between our consumerism and global depletion. But consumerism pushed by craving, hatred, and delusion is at the core of the problem and threatens life on the planet as we know it.

The Eye Is Burning

The eye is burning with the smog of pollution in Los Angeles, Beijing, New Delhi, and other cities across the world. The eye is burning with the pollution of fossil fuel usage. The eye is burning with the smoke from rainforests on fire in the Amazon, Peru, Indonesia, and elsewhere. The eye is burning with the smoldering and sizzling forms of the body parts of billions of sentient beings on grills and stoves around the world. The eyes of residents who live near factory farms are literally burning when the acidic residue in the air from lagoons of antibiotics, feces, and urine is pushed toward them by the wind. The visual consciousness is burning with the craving and hunger for cows, pigs, chickens, cow's milk, cheese, yogurt, seafood, fish, and eggs. Visual impression is burning with the desire to eat the cooked bodies of sentient beings whenever hunger arises and sees a "tasty" restaurant commercial on television.

The Nose Is Burning

The nose is burning with the diesel of thousands of trucks with sentient life forms on their way to slaughterhouses around the world. The nose is burning with the feces- and urine-caked floors of these same trucks, which in the U.S. alone are heading to 5,700 slaughterhouses. The nose is burning with the urine and feces of 45 head of cattle in 95 degree weather being transported from 1,200 to 1,500 miles on a trailer. The nose is burning with 200 pigs per transport in the winter in these same open trailers with wind chill factors of minus 50 degrees, going 60 miles an hour with the animals urinating and defecating in the trailers, freezing at their hooves as they are in it and lying in in this filth for 10 hours on a trip as they are frozen alive. The nose is burning with the stench of factory farming, each windowless building containing from 5,000 to 100,000 sentient life forms in hell-realm-like conditions. The nose is burning with the 500 million tons of the untreated open-air lagoons of putrid feces, urine, antibiotics, and hormones from the enslavement of 70 billion land animals on farms around the world. From the fire of delusion which connects our craving to sentient life but disconnects us from the natural empathy and compassion for ourselves and others. The nose is burning from the untreated animal feces and urine in greater quantities than all human waste. The nose is burning with the stench of cancer as it kills humans and causes the destruction of their bodies. The nose is burning from the gangrenous limbs which are dying and amputated from diabetes patients.

The Tongue Is Burning

The tongue is burning with desire for fat, laden with cholesterol and animal protein; it is burning for the taste of cheese, milk, and yogurt. It is burning with the desire for fish, seafood, and eggs. It is burning with desire for that which makes us sick with heart disease, cancer, diabetes, and obesity. The tongue is burning with each taste of palm oil associated with the destruction of rainforests, habitat loss, and orangutan death. The tongue is burning with the lies we tell each other about protein and the need to eat animals for health. The tongue is burning with the deceits we exhibit when we say we love animals and then eat them. The tongue is burning when we say we care for the earth yet with the next mouthful of food disparage and desecrate her. The tongue is burning when we take to Saka Dawa vows and then eat sardines on our salad at lunch. The tongue is burning when we are completely silent in the face of immense suffering. The insensible wagging tongues of Dharma teachers are burning, who say things like dairy cows exhibit the paramita of dana by giving milk to humans for their consumption, and it is our choice whether to consume animal products as if there is no ethical consequence.

The Body Is Burning

The bodies of screaming chickens and pigs are burning as they are dragged consciously through scalding water tanks in slaughterhouses around the world. The hands, legs, and minds of carpel tunnel–disfigured slaughterhouse workers are burning with the endless bodies they must cut up, rip, and package at ever increasing rates to supply the demand and bloodlust. The body of the general public is burning with unnecessary disease, restricted blood cells, plaques, and cholesterol. It is burning with cancer cells and with the harsh drugs used to kill those cells. It is burning from modern medicine, which hides symptoms but ignores root causes. It is burning with insulin coursing through our veins and arteries with nowhere to go. It is burning with open heart surgery, stents, and pacemakers. It is burning with amputations and ocular degeneration conditions. It is burning with delusion that animal products are necessary and good for us to eat. The bodies of 17,000 children are burning who die of starvation on a daily basis while we feed 70% of all the grain in the world to animals. The body is burning with disease, drugs, and pain.

The Mind Is Burning

The mind is burning with craving of that which makes us physically, mentally, and spiritually sick. It is burning with delusion of who we are and the connectedness we all have. It is burning with the ego of separateness, me, my, and I, when such a thing does not exist and cannot be found. The mind is burning with the lack of relationality to all things, and in doing so we kill ourselves and trillions of beings around us. Our minds are burning with the lack of interrelatedness and a nihilistic outlook to other life forms. Our minds are burning with "might makes right"; because I can catch, imprison, rape, grow and slaughter, cook, and eat you. I have the right to do so.

The world is burning because of craving, delusion, and ignorance of who we are. The world is burning due to not understanding and or accepting the cause and conditionality of all that arises. We throw off relativity and choose to bathe ourselves in:

- The burning blood of ego.
- The burning blood of animals.
- The burning blood of the land.
- The burning blood of our rivers, lakes, and oceans.
- The burning blood of the atmosphere.
- The burning blood of all animal species.
- The burning blood of all human generations to come and those with us here and now.

The Fuel of the Fire

The fuel of these fires is our basic, fundamental misperception of other sentient beings as food products. The fuel of these fires is a basic, fundamental misknowing of who and what we are. The fuel of these fires is our basic, fundamental misknowing of our dependent origination, connectivity, and emptiness. Our conditioned eyes have made us ignorant. They have deluded us. They have abandoned us. Our conditioned noses have made us ignorant, deluded, and abandoned. Our conditioned tongues have made us ignorant, deluded, and abandoned. Our conditioned bodies have made us ignorant, deluded, and abandoned. Our conditioned bodies have made us ignorant, deluded, and abandoned.

For the most part, we have been taught from early on that meat, fish, dairy, and eggs are good foods to bring into our bodies. Our eyes have been conditioned to love the brown, cooked, stuffed body of a turkey or a cow's roasted rump on our table. Our noses have been conditioned to enjoy the smell of roasted flesh. Our tongues have been conditioned to prefer the creamy, fat-laden texture and taste of cow's milk, cream, and cheese. Our minds have been conditioned to see others as food. We are conditioned to crave these things. However, it is easy to break the conditioned craving state. This is what the Buddha taught. Become aware, stop and choose the healthy, compassionate, and environmentally sound alternative—plants.

We have the ability to change in any way we wish. The Buddha and many teachers inform us the mind is luminous and clear. Luminosity gives it the ability to change wherever and whatever we would like; we simply point the mind toward it. This ability today is known scientifically as neuroplasticity. We can escape conditioned responses due to the ability of our minds to change. We simply need to choose over and over until a new healthy, ethical, compassionate, and environmentally sound habit is ingrained. Craving of some sort may never completely be eradicated while we are alive and in this body, but what we can do is train ourselves to recognize the impulse of craving meat, fish, dairy, and eggs for what it is: dukkha (suffering). We can know that when we eat it we will cause more suffering to the next animal in the consumer-driven database of supply/demand, our own health, and the planet. When we crave dairy we must remember this adds to global depletion of land, water, and oceans. When we crave fish, we must realize it adds to depletion of land, water, oceans, and our health. We don't need saturated fat. We don't need toxins. We don't want to cause the destruction of coral reefs. We don't want to be the cause of bycatch—or more accurately bykill. We don't want species extinction.

This is educated mindful consciousness rather than conditioned ignorant unconsciousness. When we choose to eat meat, fish, dairy, and eggs, we choose to live by a conditioned ignorant consciousness. This is what pervades all of us who continue to eat the bodies of sentient beings, giving ourselves disease and causing destruction of our planet. Suffering only arises out of conditioned ignorant consciousness when we allow it.

Disenchantment

The teachings of the Buddha are multi-layered. There is so much profundity incorporated within the teachings it can take a lifetime to understand a portion of them or even to understand fully one part of the Buddhist Canon, or even a single passage. The Fire Sermon has many levels of understanding. It can be described as a teaching that we can liberate ourselves from suffering by freeing ourselves from enchantment with the five senses.

Seeing ourselves ablaze with the fire of craving to eat the bodies and secretions of sentient beings, we become disenchanted. Just as the Buddha's listeners became disenchanted 2,500 years ago.

> Seeing thus, the instructed noble disciple grows disenchanted with the eye, disenchanted with forms, disenchanted with consciousness at the eye...grows disenchanted with the nose, disenchanted aromas, disenchanted with the tongue and disenchanted with flavors and disenchanted with the intellect.
> ~ Addittapariyaya Sutta

Thus disenchanted we become dispassionate with foods of flesh origin and are released from the craving of eating them. This perhaps can be considered a mini nirvana. A blowing out of craving. A freedom from conventional clinging we have been taught from childhood. A freedom to help the world and all beings rebuild, recover, and restore.

The fire sermon follows a typical teaching style of the Buddha, similar to the scientific method. He lays out a problem, then provides a possible solution and gives his students the complete freedom to test out his hypothesis. We must test if for ourselves. Buddhism is an empowering process; we must do our own work.

Do we see the problem? If we see it, are we revolted by it? Are we tired of hurting our bodies and creating global warming and depletion? Are we ready to detach from this behavior? If you are ready to stop, then do so, and be free. Be liberated from eating animals. Be free from having your health harmed. Be free from the causes of this activity that harms the earth. Blow out the fire of craving, hatred, and delusion.

This is Buddhism 101. Defining what the causes of suffering are. Becoming fed up with it when we realize it. Turning away from the causes and becoming free of them. This is how we become healthier of mind, body, and spirit and heal the planet. Define the problem, get fed up, change, and become free. Put differently:

- Embrace the fact that eating meat, fish, dairy and eggs causes disease, devastates our health, causes the death of 70 billion land animals, and 1 to 2 trillion sea animals, and is a major contributor to global depletion, extinction, and climate change.
- Let go of your attachment to meat, fish, dairy, and eggs.
- Stop eating and wearing them.
- Act as a more empathetic, compassionate force in the world who is no longer on fire with the craving, delusion, and ignorance.

We can be happy, healthy, and ethical at the same time by choosing not to eat those we say we love and wish to save. I wish you all the best in our journey toward greater empathy and compassion for all sentient beings.

Epilogue: A Dispatch From the Infusion Center

It has been a very extraordinary 2017. It started with a dream what woke me in a cold sweat with a fearful import. It was not the content of the dream, which I didn't remember, but the crystal clear final message—YOU HAVE CANCER—which was flashing like a bold marquee to my wakening mind. It was frightening! My first thought was, *Where did this come from?* The next was, *Should I listen to it?*

I thought about it for a couple days and then made an appointment for a physical with bloodwork. I told my doctor about my dream and he didn't laugh me off but informed me afterward that my physical was completely normal, and a note in my patient portal told me that bloodwork (other than hemoglobin being slightly lower than normal) was fine. Nothing to worry about.

February 5 came with the annual Jewel Heart miserable winter retreat, colloquially named that by Gelek Rimpoche and our sangha due to Michigan weather and those who came to retreat with colds and flus. The subject was Ganden Lha Gyema, a Gelupa teaching from Je Tsongkhapa. Rimpoche was in the hospital. He had been for a few weeks. He had an internal bleed that could not be stopped. We watched videos of the Ganden Lha Gyema teaching from 2005 and senior students took over discussions of the material. Having attended the 2005 retreat I was enjoying the video review, mantra recitation, and the cheerful retreat atmosphere. On Friday morning, Feb 10, I was hoping to continue with my retreat but woke up at 5:00 a.m. vomiting blood from a hemorrhage in my stomach. My wife called an ambulance and I had my first ride ever to a hospital with the lights flashing. The bleeding had stopped by the time I left, as my blood pressure plummeted. The hospital admitted me and did an endoscope to try and find the source of the bleeding and they found a 10-centimeter tumor in my stomach which was biopsied. I spent 2 days in intensive care and then 2 days in a regular room. The biopsy results came back on Monday, Feb 13, adeno carcinoma, a form of stomach cancer.

As vegan for 7 years, and not a junk food vegan who lives on pop/soda and sugar cookies, who eats a mostly WFPB diet, I was surprised I had cancer. There was no warning sign. I was not in pain prior. I didn't have one symptom. I was not on medication. This was a dharma lesson on impermanence. I remember not being concerned in the hospital ever for my life or death, I was very much at peace. But coming out of the hospital, the realization of what this meant and will mean has put my Buddhist practice to test.

Eating a vegan diet is shown to reduce the risk of cancer. This is what the science bears out, but vegans get sick too. Vegans die. From a Buddhist perspective: All conditioned phenomena are impermanent. Any phenomena that rely on causes and conditions will change. Human beings are a form of conditioned phenomena. We can die from a million different things in this life. We don't know when it's coming or how—none of us do. This has been drilled into me for the past 20 years by Gelek Rimpoche.

Meanwhile, I was told Rimpoche was very concerned for me and asked how I was doing after he heard I was in the hospital and could not complete the retreat. Here he was sick and asking for me, it was just like him to be concerned for others when he was so very sick himself.

I was released from the hospital on Monday, Feb. 13. Dazed and weak, I was happy to be released and home. However, 2 days later Rimpoche passed away, on the morning of February 15. I never got a chance to see him again, but his presence was with me in the hospital and ever since. On Feb 17 Billie and I went to visit him at the funeral home. He had not been embalmed and was in a cold room. He seemed present and even breathing, but we knew he was not. Others mentioned this, too.

A few days later, via email, I learned from Hartmut Sagolla, a senior administrator and teacher at Jewel Heart, that while in the hospital Rimpoche, on his deathbed, had named my wife Billie and I as Jewel Heart Ambassadors for Vegetarianism, Veganism, and Animal Welfare. What an honor. He realized there was a need, realized that all sentient life needed to be actively helped. In 2015 he had authorized the usage of the Jewel Heart Ann Arbor center for holding Dharma Voices for Animals group meetings. Billie and I had been having these meeting periodically since then.

I write this all from my "sick bed," being in the 14th week of intensive chemotherapy as I type these words and finish this book. I don't know if I am going to live or die from this cancer. It has though been a gift. When I am in the infusion room and interacting with the nurses and some of the patients I realize how sad it is that we are all walking around with grief and death on our faces. Everyone here has a death sentence. A part of me laughs at this, since this is the ultimate truth for us all. Outside of the hospital we all walk around with the hubris of living forever. Nothing can be further from the truth. We are, each of us, running toward our own death from the moment we are born. We all are in the cancer ward, all the time; we just do not take the time to meditate on this and incorporate it into daily awareness. Getting this cancer has been a blessing in some ways and allowed me to deepen my spiritual practice even further. I have come to realize just how profound the Buddhist teachings are and how they have impacted my outlook.

Does Anyone Else Feel Like They Are Living in Perpetual Grief?

This is a recent post from a vegan activist friend. It encompasses the very basis of our shared dilemma. It is something that burns out animal rights activists and vegans without a spiritual practice who choose to be present with the immense suffering that goes on in the animal kingdom caused by human beings. We are all walking dead. All of us. None of us gets out this life intact. Even if everyone went vegan today, and we became an organic planet, non-warring, non-misogynistic, a wholesome caring species, sharing planet, and its resources, we would all end up dying. Everyone we love. Everything we love. All the animals and people, because all created phenomena are impermanent.

But we look out at the world—with eyes that are seeing—with a sense of permanence. We feel every moment as permanent, and we feel like we are going to live forever. We don't want anyone to take this from us. We don't want to face up to the fact this is the perpetual grief we are living in. In the cancer infusion ward, I am surrounded by people who didn't want to get cancer but here they find themselves fighting as best they know how, trying to cling to life will all their strength. None of us are different in this, and this is the ancient First Noble Truth, the truth of suffering. But we need to flip this around and realize the cause of it is our attachment to something that cannot go on. We need to let go of the clinging to the perpetual grief. We are so fortunate to be able to see the perpetual grief. It is a gift. A spiritual divinely grounded gift, if we choose to do something with it. The present is permanent. We, in this body, are not. The past is a figment of our cognition, as is the future. We only have the present moment. It's all we ever had and ever will have. When we embrace the present, grief subsides.

Perpetual grief, while not a good feeling, is a great spiritual first step. It brings many of us out of the sleep we are in to seek relief in some form. Perpetual grief is a mode of awakening, experiencing the First Noble Truth, the truth of suffering. Not everyone experiences it, and even if one feels it, most cannot identify what it is and what to do about it.

Attachment and aversion run the process. Analyze why we are feeling this way.

For a vegan activist, someone who desperately wants to make this world a better place for humans and animals, it is tough to see the perpetual agony that happens all around. Yet, we must not get attached to the agony but see the blessing this ability has given us. We have been given an opportunity to do some good in the world. What more of a gift is there? To be awakened to the horrors of this lifetime on this planet but see the beauty at that same time and have the capacity to help if we choose to do so.

"Precious human life gained but once has great potential but is easily lost. Empower me to take advantage of this and to think day and night of taking its essence. I must remember that spirit quivers in the flesh like a bubble in the water and after death one's evil deeds trail after one like a shadow trails the body."

I am bolstered and supported by these words from Tshongkhapa in the Foundations of All Perfections. Life, all lives are gained but once and lost. All mammals die. All insects die. All human beings die. However, those of us with minds and capacity to see and feel the perpetual grief can do something about this. We can take the long view. The real truth is nothing ends. We all go on but in a changed and different form. The reason we see with permanent eyes is twofold, one is based on ego attached to an idea that we are forever and the other is our true self knowing we are spiritual beings which will continue after death. What to do is live with the highest morality we can, being as generous as we can, helping as many lives as we can, dropping judgement of others, even our so-called enemies, and look at them with thankfulness. We all live in rented apartments. None of us get out with the money we made or the things we accumulated. All is left behind when our body dies. But what goes on carries with it our moral and immoral deeds. We carry our good and bad deeds, and this is what leads us to the next adventure.

When we do something to help others in this life it leads us up the spiritual karmic ladder. This is what we should be focusing on, making a difference in the lives of others to help them awaken and live a more meaningful life.

What to do? Go out into nature, take your shoes off and walk in the grass. Get grounded in the reality of impermanence. It's OK, we are all going to die and it is completely natural. Find a tree and hug it. Feel the ancient energy that comes from the earth through its roots and feel the sun that sustains it, creating the eternal connection between earth, sky, and sun. We are part of this energy field. This earth is a life-creating phenomenon. We are part of it and it is part of us. We have nothing to grieve and everything to be happy about. We are awake, we are moral, we think, feel, and want positive change. Meditate on this. This is wisdom coming to us from our past good deeds. It will take us forward to do more good work and allow us to reborn again to continue our work. What a gift to be in perpetual grief because it gives us the ability to see the connections between us all, we see we are one, and there is no separation. All phenomena are devoid of self-existence. The eyes of the pig, cow, or chicken on the slaughterhouse truck looking back at us are our own eyes. We know this in our heart. We can do something about this. This is a blessing, not a curse. It is our job to help others see this and awaken to do less harm and more good in this world. This is the essence of the Buddhist path. This awareness can lead to nirvana and peace. This is the essence of the vegan path. This is the Buddhist First Precept of do less harm, do not kill, respect all life, and practice Ahimsa.

Find a way to put a daily meditation practice into place. For me this has been a Buddhist path, but any meditation from any tradition will work. Be honest with yourself. If your meditation is based on kindness, love, and compassion it will lead to right action. If your intention is based on kindness, love, and compassion it will lead to right action.

Find ways to express yourself. Find a group to get involved with and focus our energies. There are two examples in the back of this book: Dharma Voices for Animals and the Plant Based Nutrition Support Group. Get involved but not discouraged. This is a long-term battle. From my perspective it will take many lifetimes, and we who see the need must take action. This is a form of generosity. This will help us to cultivate positive mental attitudes and transform perpetual grief into something beautiful.

In the end it doesn't matter what we die from or that we died, it matters how we lived. How we changed and how awakened we became. It matters that we learned to kill less and practiced nonviolence in earnest. It matters that we learned to respect all life.

It doesn't matter what a vegan died from or that a vegan died, what matters is who they didn't kill due to their lifestyle of not eating animals, wearing animals, going to entertainment which uses animals, and abstaining from products which use animals for testing. "I must remember that spirit quivers in the flesh like a bubble in the water and after death one's evil deeds trail after one like a shadow trails the body." And what follows a vegan lifestyle? Good deeds follow us into the next adventure that shadows this life.

I don't know if this cancer will kill me or not. I don't know if it will spread throughout my entire body or not. I don't know what will happen. I know I will die either from this disease or something else. But whenever that time comes I will be happy that I became a person who caused a little less harm in this world. I will be happy I was married to the same wonderful woman in a committed relationship for 40 years. I will be happy I raised beautiful daughters and was a father who was with them, always available, and supported them my entire life. I will be happy I was no longer responsible for animals being tortured, mutilated, exploited, and slaughtered. I will be happy I became a Vegan-Buddhist who came to truly understand what animals need from me; seeing them as persons and someone rather than a something. I will be happy I finally came to realize the qualities all sentient lifeforms have; a will of their own, preferences, consciousness, appreciation for their own life, character, personality, complexity, courage, and emotions. I will be happy I stopped seeing chickens as defined by their ability to lay eggs, their breasts, legs, and other body parts. I will be happy I stopped believing and living as someone who was somehow superior to animals, OK with their exploitation and murder because they are not one of us. I will be happy I began seeing clothes, shoes, and furniture as the skin, wool, and hair of someone who wanted to live. I will be happy I began connecting with who and whom these animals were before they became the dismembered body parts and secretions we call eggs, dairy, and leather. I will be happy my environmental footprint was lessoned including energy, water, carbon dioxide, and land. I will be happy I encouraged humans to consider better health and their relationship to food, animals, and the planet. I will be happy I was able to change my habitual mind from controlling my life in this area and used meditation to free my cravings for animal flesh. I will be happy that as a vegan I gave up nothing and learned to stop taking what was never mine to take. I will be happy I took responsibility for my own actions. I will be happy I became a Vegan-Buddhist and I hope other Buddhist practitioners and leaders will follow. I now understand what sentience truly means at a much deeper level and this is the compassionate jewel-like quality of being a Vegan-Buddhist.

Dedication

And just as in all Tibetan Buddhist teachings that I have attended, at the end of the teaching or retreat, we dedicate the merit received. I dedicate any merit of this book to all sentient beings, any merit the book can give, any merit anyone receives reading this book, and any merit that improves the planet and improves the lives of animals. If just one animal's life has become spared by someone skipping a meal of meat, then this book has been worth the time and effort spent writing and publishing it. May they all sentient beings become fully enlightened, may they be free from suffering, may they dwell in equanimity, happy and at peace. May we cover them with our only blanket even if we become cold. May we take the pain and misery onto ourselves even though it hurts us badly. May we recognize them all as mother sentient beings who have been our fellow travelers for countless eons. May we free them from all ignorance by giving away to them all that we have to offer.

Thank You

I dedicate this book (and series) to my wife Billie, who has supported my efforts to be a better person all these years, who supported this crazy idea to write about veganism and Buddhism, who has been by my soul mate and at my side for 38 years of marriage. She has always sustained my efforts to try and improve. Thank you Billie! And also to my daughters, Stephanie and Cristina, who courageously brought the plight of animals to the forefront of our family and generously helped in early beta readings and editing of this manuscript. I love and appreciate you both so much. Without Billie, Stephanie, and Cristina, I would not be on this path and this book would not exist.

Thank you to Elizabeth Hurwitz, who also read a very early draft of this manuscript, made suggestions, and supplied encouragement. Also to Sherry Morgado, Tashi Nyima, and Vicki Seglin, final beta readers, thank you for your time, comments, and assistance. Your activism and caring for the plight of humans, animals, and the planet exemplifies the behavior of a Bodhisattva.

I must express deep appreciation for T. Colin Campbell, Richard Oppenlander, and Sherry Morgado for granting me your time and allowing me to interview you and publish your insights into health, food, and the plight we humans find ourselves in today.

To my editor, Michele Truty, I am so very thankful to have found you and feel blessed when our paths crossed. Your insight and thoughtfulness of the writing process, knowledge of main Buddhist tenets, and being a vegan has proven invaluable, akin to a wish-fulfilling gem in Tibetan Buddhist lore. Thank you for all you have done to help me bring this work to fruition.

Lastly, I want to thank my late teacher, Gelek Rimpoche, from the bottom of my heart and express my sincere gratitude for his tireless teaching activities. Having spent countless hours in retreats with him since 1997, what little I understand about Buddhism is due to his kindness. Gelek Rimpoche is the founder of Jewel Heart, a Tibetan Buddhist learning center with chapters around the world, including of all places Ann Arbor, Michigan. Rimpoche passed away on February 15, 2017. He is missed by all.

Contact and Website:

john.bussineau@gmail.com

thebuddhatheveganandyou.com

Appendix A: Interview with a vegan Buddhist nutritionist

Bussineau: Good morning. Thanks for the interview, Sherry. Before we start talking about nutrition, can you tell me something about your background?

Morgado: Sure, let me give you a little bit from the beginning of my life. I grew up in the Central Valley of California on a farm where we raised animals—particularly cows that were going to be slaughtered.

My grandparents had immigrated to the United States from Portugal, but when I was growing up, like most everyone, I ate a standard American diet—with a pretty heavy emphasis on meat, dairy, and eggs. But we did also have a healthy Mediterranean emphasis in my family on beans and vegetables. I think that was an important start to my interest in nutrition.

I became a vegetarian for the first time when I was 9 years old, when I came home from school one day because I was sick and I saw one of our cows being slaughtered. That happened to be the day that one of them had been selected to be slaughtered, and that had a tremendous impact on me, as a child. It was really my moment of awakening, and I understood what was happening to these animals and I understood the food on my plate a little bit better. So that was the first time I became a vegetarian. It set the stage for me, in terms of the spiritual path that I ended up eventually choosing and the dietary habits I've picked up.

I've been practicing Buddhism now for close to 6 years and I practice in the Vietnamese tradition of Thích Nhất

Hạnh, who is a very well-known vegan monk and peace activist.

Bussineau: Are you a vegan now?

Morgado: Yes, an ethical vegan. When I became vegan for ethical reasons, I also decided I wanted to know as much as I could about vegan nutrition, because I wanted to know how to eat a diet that was going to be the best for me to stay healthy. I already knew I wasn't going to be giving up anything in terms of variety or flavor, but I really wanted to know as much as I could about nutrition so I could educate myself and talk to others.

So, the first thing I did was I completed the plant-based nutrition online course with Dr. T. Colin Campbell's Center for Nutrition Studies. It's about a six-week course that introduces you to all of the health and protective benefits of a plant-based diet. Then, when I completed that, I just wanted to know more. I decided to go on and enroll in a two-year certificate program in plant-based nutrition offered through Bauman College, a private college here in the United States. I became a nutrition consultant after I finished that two-year program.

In addition, as a result of a committed yoga practice, along the way, I actually formally studied Ayurveda, the traditional system of healing in India, Tibet, Nepal, and Sri Lanka. I became an Ayurvedic health educator.

Bussineau: That's very interesting. How did Ayurveda inform you about plant-based eating?

Morgado: Well, Ayurveda also emphasizes a plant-based diet as the optimal diet for both our physical health and our spiritual well-being. Ayurveda, just like any holistic system from the East, realizes and recognizes that the human being—and all beings—are body, mind, and spirit, and that those things cannot be separated in any way. It looks at a vegetarian diet as the best for physical health but also the best for spiritual health because it looks at the effect of our food choices on the world around us, on the sentient beings around us, and on our own karma—that's a big component of the reason for vegetarianism in Ayurveda.

For me, it brought together that Eastern spiritual perspective that's really important to me. You know, as I'm talking to people about their diet, and coaching them and educating them, it's an important component to think about. How we feel, not just physically but also emotionally and spiritually is extremely important.

Bussineau: I completely agree. When I became vegan, I really found that my Buddhist practice and my new vegan way of eating allowed me to match the inside of me to the outside of me.

Morgado: Exactly, exactly. What I found for myself was much more peace when I completely cut all animal products out of my diet. I knew that I was no longer contributing to harm or that I was minimizing the harm to the greatest extent possible that I could. It's just a tremendous feeling of peace, wholeness, and joy and an ability to really open ourselves up to everything that's going on in the world in a way that we couldn't before because we were having to shield ourselves from that violence that we were participating in.

Bussineau: After the traumatic slaughter of a cow when you were 9 years old you went vegetarian; when did you go vegan?

Morgado: I became vegan nine years ago. It was the Easter of 2007, I remember exactly when it was!

Easter was symbolic for me in a lot of ways. Chicken's eggs were the last thing that I removed from my diet when I became vegan. Eggs were, as I was growing up in a Portuguese-American culture, a really significant part of our diet. It's just part of the traditional cuisine and eggs are used very extensively. So that was a big part of my diet as a child and growing up.

I can remember, it was literally the day before Easter, and I was sitting at my kitchen table and I was looking out onto my backyard, where I have this birdfeeder. I noticed that I had a family of birds, it was clear it was the mother and the father and some babies that just hatched. I was really watching how sweetly they engaged with each other. This mother and father and baby birds, the love that they were clearly exhibiting for each other, the care that the parents were showing in taking care of their babies.

And it just struck me, very profoundly, that I would never go into my backyard and take the eggs out of these birds' nest and eat them—I would not do that. But I was doing that with chickens, in fact, I was doing worse than that! I was participating in this system that was far more cruel and violent by eating chickens' eggs. That was my big epiphany and it happened to be the day before Easter. Of course, there's the symbolism of eggs and birth in Easter, so it just kind of all came together. That just happened to be the day. That was the event—that was the epiphany that I had. I just said to myself, "Ok, I'm not going to eat these anymore." That's when I gave them up.

Bussineau: I also remember the day when I went vegan, too. I've talked to other people who have changed to a vegan plant-based diet and they also remember the very day that they did it.

Morgado: Yes, I think there's just something so significant that just wakes up inside of us and says, "Enough! I'm not going to do this anymore." Like you said, my behavior and my beliefs are not in harmony, and I want to be in harmony. It happens. Then it's not forced; it just happens so naturally and it's a beautiful thing.

Bussineau: As a vegan, I've been asked so many times about protein. The standard question is: Where do you get your protein? Can you tell me, from a nutritional standpoint, all about protein? What is it? Can we get our protein needs from plants?

Morgado: Yes, of course this is the question we hear the most.

I think it's really important that we demystify protein, and look at what it really is. In our culture in particular, in the United States and Western cultures in general, protein is equated really with meat, eggs, and dairy. That's what people think of. They think "I need to eat some protein" and they think of one of those three food groups.

Those are just the animal-based sources of protein and they are certainly not the only protein sources in the whole, huge variety of food that we have available.

The first thing, I think, when it comes to breaking this down and demystifying it, is understanding that, from a biochemical point of view, protein is made up of molecules, known as amino acids. Many people have heard of amino acids, even though they may not know what they really are. These amino acids contain things like carbon, hydrogen, oxygen, nitrogen, and sometimes sulphur, in various amounts.

These amino acids that are made up of these elements are the building blocks of protein. Think about the small building blocks that children play with—those wooden blocks. It's the individual blocks that come together to build something; in this case, the amino acids build protein. You can also think of them as puzzle pieces that fit together to make protein.

So the interesting thing is that our human body can make most of the amino acids that it needs to make protein. We actually have the biochemical processes inherent in our bodies that can make most of these amino acids. Your body is a protein-making factory.

Bussineau: That is amazing, I did not know that!

Morgado: Yeah, it is! Again, I think this is where demystifying protein is really important. I think so many of us have been taught is that the only place we can get this stuff is by eating animal flesh, in particular.

Bussineau: That's what I always thought.

Morgado: The animals, their own bodies have produced it, right? It's important to recognize that a lot of the animals that we eat are primarily plant-eaters. Whether you look at chickens or cows, pigs or turkeys. The animals that most humans eat actually eat plants and their bodies are making that protein.

We'll get back to that in just a minute...

When you look at these amino acids and the fact that your body is able to make most of them, it is important to recognize something called essential amino acids. There are nine of these that we have to take in from our food because these are the nine that our bodies cannot make. Again, many people have heard of essential amino acids, and it refers to these nine.

Bussineau: So those are the nine we cannot make?

Morgado: Exactly. They're called "essential" or sometimes "indispensable" because of the fact that we have to get them from our diet.

But I think the important thing to know, and the good news in all of this, is that all nine of the essential amino acids are available in plant food—they do not just exist in animal food, they exist in plant food.

So, the bottom line, the answer your question is: Yes, we can get all of our protein needs from plants. We don't have any need for any animal flesh or eggs or their secretions from milk to get these proteins. It's just absolutely unnecessary.

Bussineau: Along those lines, years ago I read a book and I don't remember the authors—it was a husband and wife team—and they talked about combining of foods. I've also read it in other books too, that you've got to combine certain kinds of plant foods together in order to get the right mix of nutrients. Is that really necessary?

Morgado: It's not. I know exactly what you're talking about. It might have first been referred to in a book called Diet for Small Planet, in the 1970s; I think that's probably the first place where it was referred to. It's interesting because that book was actually recommending a vegetarian diet in order to save the planet, but it also had a little bit of misinformation in it about food combining. It was corrected years later, but by then this myth became "fact" and was propagated through the years.

What this idea of combining foods really refers to the idea of a "complete protein." That's another thing people might have heard of, a complete protein. What the term "complete protein" refers to is those nine essential amino acids that we have to get from food. That's really what it's referring to. If a food contains all nine of these, in a ratio that mimics the protein in the human body, then it's called a complete protein.

So, if a person ingests animal flesh, that animal flesh has nine of those essential amino acids in a ratio that mimics exactly what human protein is in a body—when our body manufactures those proteins, it's manufacturing something that's equivalent to what's in that animal flesh.

But the important thing, again, to remember is that all amino acids come from plants. That's really the source of all of our nutrients, that's where they originally come from. As I mentioned, most of the animals that humans eat, typically are plant-eaters. When you look at, cows, chickens, turkeys, pigs—the animals used most often for food—they are plant-eaters. They are naturally herbivores, they're not carnivores. They're getting their amino acids from the plants that they eat.

When you consider that all amino acids originally come from plants and all nine of these essential amino acids are contained in plants, then we know that we can get complete proteins from plants. The only difference between the animal foods and the plant foods is that the ratios can vary in individual plant foods. So, for example, beans or legumes are a very good source of an amino acid lysine—that's one of the nine essential amino acids. But grains tend to be low in lysine. So, if you ate nothing but grains, your diet would be somewhat lacking in lysine.

But the fact is, most people don't eat just one food; most people eat a variety of foods. Especially on a plant-based diet, if you're eating this wide variety of foods, then your body is just going to naturally take in all of those amino acids that you need in order to form complete proteins.

Again, getting back to the fact that some plant foods may be high in certain amino acids and low in others—this is the fact that was used in the past, this rationale for the necessity to combine foods at each meal. This idea of beans and rice being combined together, for example, being one of the most well-known combinations.

Bussineau: Can you expand on that a little more?

Morgado: For example, beans are high in lysine and rice is low. Whereas rice is a little higher in methionine and beans are a little lower in that. So, you combine them together and you're getting just the right ratio that you need. That was the idea behind food combining, but here's the important update to all of this: What we know now is that our liver actually stores the amino acids from the food that we digested earlier in the day. It stores them and then releases these amino acids as they are needed throughout the day to combine with the new foods that we've eaten.

So, at breakfast we have a meal, maybe we have oatmeal, soy milk, and some fruit, for example. Our body digests that and some of the amino acids, for example, from the soy milk or the oatmeal, our body is just going to go ahead and process those and store them in our liver. Then, later on in the day we have a green salad and some lentil soup—for lunch. We might have some fruit for a snack and at dinner, we have tempeh, and some quinoa, and some steamed kale and carrots. So, we've got these amino acids that our body processed earlier in the day, that have been stored in our liver, and then we continue to eat throughout the day and more amino acids are going through our digestive system, into our bloodstream, into our liver.

The great thing, again, is that our body is able to take what it stored in the liver and combine it with these new foods, break everything down, and reassemble it to make the protein that we need.

Bussineau: That's amazing! I didn't know that our liver actually stored amino acids. That's very interesting.

Morgado: Right! So, again, it is not necessary to combine foods at each meal but it's kind of a traditional thing—a lot of cultures do that—and there's nothing wrong with it. If you enjoy combining foods, and it tastes good, and it provides that satiation, that's fantastic. But it's not something we need to be worried about in terms of getting protein.

Bussineau: What kinds of combining foods do other cultures do? I know, coming from an Italian household, we had a lot of beans and pasta, Pasta Fasu, my grandmother used to combine greens and beans a lot of the time. Are there other combinations that you're aware of?

Morgado: Yes, there are thousands of combinations. Probably the ones that we're the most familiar with are the combination of the legume or bean and some form of a grain—this would be one of the more common ones. So, for example, in Southeast Asia: tofu and rice. In Ethiopia: lentils and teff—either teff made into injera (the teff bread) or even as the whole grain. In Egypt it's common to eat fava beans and millet together. Of course, throughout India, Nepal, Bhutan, Sri Lanka, the countries in that region: dal, which really refers to any beans or lentils, those are often combined with rice or flatbreads. Even in Europe: bean soup with bread or bean soup with pasta, or bean soup with oat cakes in Scotland. That would be another combination. And, of course, in Central

America, again, lots of emphasis on legumes and beans with rice, quinoa, or some form of a tortilla. Those would be some examples.

Bussineau: How much protein do we actually need each day, and why?

Morgado: Well, our needs overall are actually much lower than most people think. Like you said, there's been a tremendous emphasis on protein in our culture, in particular. Certainly it varies by gender—men need a little bit more than women do, adults need a little bit more than children do, and our degree of activity, to a certain extent, can dictate that.

The average adult needs about 55–70 grams daily. Just by way of comparison, in the United States, the actual average consumption is 90 grams for men and 62 grams for women. Again, except in the case of an extreme athlete that needs to build muscle, most men don't need more than 70 grams daily and the average actual consumption is 90—quite a bit higher than what our bodies actually need.

Having said that, it's important for someone who's on a plant-based diet, or considering it, to be aware that while you definitely don't need to be obsessed about protein intake, you do need to think about it and make certain that you're including some forms of more concentrated sources of plant protein in your diet, because protein does play a vital role in our health.

Our body needs protein to make and repair our bodily tissues. They function as enzymes, and hormones, and components of our genes. Protein is a macronutrient that we need, we just don't need it in excess.

Bussineau: Do our bodies use protein for energy?

Morgado: That is another thing we often hear about that protein is needed for energy. Protein is not generally used for energy, unless it's the body's last resort. Our body actually burns carbohydrates as its preferred source of fuel for energy first. Then it would burn fat and then lastly it would burn protein. Again, protein is for building and repairing of tissue, predominantly—plus those other things that I had mentioned—but not really for energy. Unprocessed carbohydrates are what our body likes to burn for energy.

Bussineau: Are there ratios that you would recommend for carbohydrates, proteins, and fats?

Morgado: There is some variation by individual because, obviously, what we need depends in part on our age, it depends on our activity level, and sometimes some people just find they feel a little bit better when they eat a little more protein, for example, or a little less fat.

In general, it is recommended that the preponderance of your calories come from carbohydrates—this would be carbohydrates that come from unrefined foods, whole foods. So this is about 50–75% of calories from carbohydrates. Then, the next would be fats and that would be about 15–30% of calories from fat. Finally, about 10–20% from protein.

Again, this varies by individual so there might be someone who feels the best at the high end of protein and low end of the carbohydrate range—fifty percent from carbohydrates and twenty percent from protein. Then, somebody else may find that the reverse works better for them—higher end of the carbohydrate intake and lower end of protein. I think it's good, in general, to recognize that that's the order our body functions the most efficiently on, because mostly what we need for energy are those complex carbohydrates.

Bussineau: When I turned vegan and began reading about nutrition, I was amazed to find out that protein was in almost every plant food I could think of. Some are, obviously, higher in protein than others. I was startled to find out that even a banana has protein in it. Can you talk about the various amounts of protein in various kinds of foods?

Morgado: Yes, as you mentioned: All whole and unrefined foods—the only exception is oil, like olive oil, or canola oil, or sunflower oil—all plant foods contain some amount of protein. This includes vegetables and it even includes fruit. At the top, in terms of protein content, would be beans and legumes—this would also include all soy products, like tempeh, tofu, and soy milk, edamame, as well as vegan meats made from soy, wheat or other grains and vegetables. These are really at the very, very top, in terms of protein content. These have about twenty to forty percent of their total calories from protein.

Then, also, looking at vegetables, vegetables average ten to thirty-seven percent of calories from protein. For example, broccoli, kale, and collards have about three grams of protein in each serving—that's about three-and-a-half ounces. That's really pretty high. Nuts and seeds are also extremely high in protein. They have anywhere from fourteen percent to twenty-six grams per three-and-a-half ounce serving.

When you consider the fact that virtually every plant food, except for oils, has some amount of protein in it and there are plant sources that are very high in protein, there's an abundant amount of protein available in these foods to meet all of our nutrition needs.

Bussineau: Is there any rule that you would give for vegans in order to get enough protein?

Morgado: The first thing is, if you're eating enough calories to maintain your weight and you're eating a really varied diet—you're eating a variety of plant-based foods—you're probably getting enough protein. It is important, as I mentioned earlier, to give it a little bit of consideration though. Although protein deficiency really does not occur in industrialized countries, you never hear about somebody having protein deficiency, there is the potential for someone to have a suboptimal protein intake, where their health isn't as supported as it could be.

We do recommend that everyone get a minimum of three servings a day of legumes, beans, peanuts, and/or soy foods. Veggie meat can be included in that group even though those are more highly processed. If you are reducing your calorie intake in order to lose weight, or you're over the age of fifty, then you want to increase your intake of those particular foods to five servings a day.

So, if your diet is varied, not only are you going to get enough protein, but it's also important to recognize that in those foods that you're eating that have protein, you're getting a lot of fiber, vitamins, minerals, antioxidants. You're getting that complete package of everything you need to be healthy.

Bussineau: I'm going to change gears a little bit to vitamins and minerals. I've read various opinions on whether we need them if we eat a varied diet of whole foods. I personally do take a multivitamin a few days a week, not every day. I know that I've read over and over again that we need vitamin B12. Can you speak to this?

What is vitamin B12? Where does it come from? Why can't I get vitamin B12 eating a WFPB diet?

Morgado: I agree; I also take a plant-based multivitamin a few days a week. I take vitamin B12 every day. B12, to answer your question, is a water-soluble vitamin, meaning that if we take in more than our body needs, we can excrete it out through the urine. So there is no concern of getting too much.

B12 is important for several reasons. First, our bodies need it to convert food into energy, so it's a tremendous support for energy production. It also helps to produce red blood cells in our bone marrow, protects our nerve fibers, and helps our body get rid of homocysteine. Homocysteine is by-product of the breakdown of protein in the body. Homocysteine is important because it's been implicated in heart disease. So B12 performs all of those essential functions.

In terms of where it comes from, it's really interesting! B12 is produced by bacteria—that's the ultimate source of B12. It's not an inherent micronutrient that can be found in roots, leaves, or the stalks of fruits or plants, the parts of plants that we eat. Because it's bacteria derived, it used to be common in the soil that we would grow those plants in. So, it used to be plentiful in the soil and, in the past, we actually ate a bit more soil than we eat now! Some soil always clings to vegetables and fruits and we really wash and scrub our fruits and vegetables far more than we did in the past. We have some legitimate reasons for that, because of concerns about pesticides, for example. So this pesticide use has done two things: It's depleted these bacteria in the soil and it's caused us to wash and scrub our foods pretty thoroughly. So that bacteria doesn't really exist anymore in our soil.

Therefore, it doesn't really have the opportunity to cling to our food and what is there, we wash away.

The other thing is that, because it's a bacteria, it is also produced in the intestines of animals where it will make its way into animal tissue and secretions. Whatever B12 exists in flesh of animals and in animal foods is because, again, it's produced in their intestines. So, if you're eating a pure plant-based diet, there's really no way to get an adequate amount of B12, because you're not eating animal flesh and it's really not in our soil anymore.

You will hear that fermented foods—things like sauerkraut, or kimchi, yogurt, kombucha, things like that—are often touted as being good sources of B12. The issues there is that they may indeed contain some B12 that's produced through the fermentation process, but they're not reliable sources. It's not that they don't contain B12, it's just that it's not a reliable source as there's no way to control how much B12 is in any particular fermented food.

Bussineau: Can we rely on B12-fortified foods?

Morgado: There are many B12-fortified foods such as nutritional yeast, plant-based milks, and vegan meats. People vary in the amount of those foods that they eat, if they eat those foods at all. What it really comes down to is that the only reliable source of B12 is a supplement. This is true both for vegans and for meat-eaters—that's an important point to emphasize! B12 deficiency and the risk for that is not just an issue for vegans, it's an issue for everyone because of the way we've depleted this bacteria in our soil, as I mentioned.

Also, anyone over the age of 50, regardless of the type of diet that they're eating, is probably not synthesizing B12 very well. We lose our ability to synthesize it the older we get, due to changes in our stomach acid. Everyone over the age of 50 is recommended to take a B12 supplement, regardless of diet.

Bussineau: Are there deficiencies we can get from not having enough B12?

Morgado: Yes, and it is a serious condition. It can cause anemia, it can cause nerve damage, gastrointestinal disturbances, and, as I mentioned earlier, elevated blood levels of homocysteine.

Bussineau: OK, this sounds critical and something we ought to pay attention to!

Morgado: The importance of this is that the nerve damage can be permanent if the deficiency is not caught and it continues. Homocysteine is seriously implicated in heart disease—probably just as much of a risk factor as high cholesterol can be.

Those are the reasons why it's important. I think it's important to know that supplementing is very easy and it's affordable—B12 supplements are not expensive. Also, the amounts that we need are relatively small—we just need four to seven micrograms a day, it is not a lot.

Bussineau: What's the recommended daily dose?

Morgado: Currently, the recommendation for B12 is that you take 25–100 micrograms daily, or two thousand to twenty-five hundred micrograms twice a week. B12 comes in two forms: methylcobalamin and cyanocobalamin. Cyanocobalamin is recommended as its conversion process makes it more available and absorbable by our body. If you take an excess of those recommended dosage, as I mentioned, it's not harmful. Your body will excrete it if it doesn't need it.

Bottom line is definitely do take a B12 supplement. Find one that you like, they come in different forms: liquid or tablets that you place under the tongue, they're called sublingual. The belief with those is that those might be better absorbed because they go straight into the bloodstream, they don't go through the digestive system. But, it's also fine to take a pill or a capsule as well. Find one that works for you and take it. The other recommendation is, at least on an annual basis, have your doctor test your B12 levels.

Bussineau: Another question vegans get asked quite often surrounds calcium. There's a worry when people go to plant-based lifestyle that they're not going to get enough calcium to keep their bones strong. Do we need to get calcium from cows milk?

Morgado: No, we don't. Just like protein, I think it's important to demystify what calcium is and where it originally comes from. The bottom line is that calcium is a mineral and minerals come, first and foremost, from soil and from plants, not from animals. Plants pick up the minerals from the soil that they grow in and when those plants decompose, they put minerals back into the soil. Animal food contains minerals because the animals eat plants. That's the bottom line.

You can get all the calcium you need by eating plants. You don't have to consume the product of the animal that ate the plant, which is the original source. The other thing is that plant sources of calcium perform other functions, as they tend to be high in other nutrients important for bone health, like potassium, vitamin C, and vitamin K.

Another interesting point about calcium is that what matters is how much your body actually absorbs. The average person only absorbs about 25–30% of the calcium that they take in. Minerals can be hard to absorb in the body. This is normal. The important thing about calcium from plants is that it's been found to be more what we call "bioavailable" to the human body than calcium from cow's milk or goat's milk.

Bussineau: Ok. Can you unpack bioavailable for us?

Morgado: What bioavailable means is the degree to which our body can absorb and utilize the nutrient we're taking in. So, in this case, with calcium from plants, it's been found that our bodies can actually better absorb and utilize the calcium from plants.

For example, the average plant food—let's take broccoli and kale, for example—50–60% of its calcium is actually absorbed by the human body. The percentage for cow's milk is 30%.

So, when you're taking in your calcium from plant sources, your body's actually absorbing more of it. And you're getting those other nutrients that also support bone health, so you're getting more of a complete package in terms of support of bone health.

Bussineau: I've read before that we excrete more calcium than we bring in and most of the calcium we bring in is excreted, so this could relate to the bioavailability but could it also be related to the fact that animal foods are acidic in nature? Do acidic foods cause issues, too?

Morgado: There's a certain amount of controversy about that. The studies that I've read indicate that because of the different biochemical composition of animal foods, they do tend to be more acidic than alkaline. Our bodies need a certain alkaline-acidity balance and alkaline foods, in general, are found to be more health-promoting. A predominantly alkaline environment in our body lends itself to the best possible health. There is a theory that acidic blood causes calcium to be leached from the bones, as the body attempts to establish a more alkaline environment. We tend to have fewer problems with inflammation and fewer problems with viruses and bacteria when our body's a little more alkaline.

One other thing about cow's milk, in particular. And Dr. Campbell talks about this pretty extensively in _The China Study,_ is that the protein that's in cow's milk, which is called "casein," can really bind up, tie up, the calcium that is available in cow's milk and not make it available. The casein actually causes other problems for our health.

So, we don't get any of those harmful substances from green, leafy vegetables and cruciferous vegetables. We don't get that harmful casein; they tend to be more alkaline, their calcium is more available, and they have all these other nutrients. So, for that reason, they're a better source.

Bussineau: Can you describe what the best plant sources of calcium are? And which are your go-to foods?

Morgado: Number one, top of the list is green, leafy vegetables. So these would be things like kale, collards, mustard greens, turnip greens, Chinese cabbage, bok choy, also vegetables like broccoli. Soaked nuts and seeds, almonds and almond butter, and tahini, from sesame seeds.

As well as calcium from tofu. When tofu is made from soy milk,the coagulating agent is often calcium sulfate or some other form of calcium. So, we get calcium from tofu, as well.

I focus on green leafy vegetables and eating a variety of them is really important because we get different levels of calcium and we get different nutrients and it also makes our diet more interesting and exciting. I use green leafy vegetables the most.

There's also fortified plant-based milks and juices available. I don't use those extensively, but that's another source of calcium.

One thing about those green leafy vegetables that I should mention: there are some leafy greens that are very healthy but they're not the best sources of calcium, and those are spinach, chard, and beet greens.

The reason why is: they have a lot of oxalates in them— oxalic acid—and this binds up calcium, so it's not so bioavailable. They're not the best sources of calcium, still very healthy, still have lots of other nutrients. You should still include them in your diet, but don't really depend on those for your calcium.

Bussineau: Sounds like many of the best calcium sources are also the best protein sources.

Morgado: Yes! That's the wonderful thing about plant food. You get such a variety of nutrients with all of these foods. If you're eating, for example, a chicken breast, what a person is getting from that is fat, protein, and cholesterol.

They're not getting anything else. There's no fiber, no minerals, and virtually no vitamins. They're pretty void of those things. Whereas, when you're eating all of these amazing plant foods, they all have this package of nutrients in them. There's not just one single nutrient that you're getting from a plant food, there's many nutrients…I think Dr. Campbell likens it to a symphony, as I recall from one of our teachings. He was talking about, "It's more beautiful to go listen to a symphony orchestra playing than necessarily one instrument, right?"

Bussineau: That makes a lot of sense! So based on our conversation, I've learned that there are a lot of advantages to this way of eating: I can get all of my protein needs met by eating plants; I can get my calcium needs met by eating plants; and if I take a B12 supplement and eat enough calories in a varied diet, I can not only survive but probably thrive pretty well on a vegan diet. Can you talk a little bit about the advantages or benefits of a whole-foods vegan diet as opposed to the standard American diet?

Morgado: Definitely. There are so many scientific studies out there, numerous scientific studies that have shown that a plant-based diet provides us with significant protective health advantages. Most of these relate to minimizing the risk to chronic diseases, such as cardiovascular disease, Type II diabetes, obesity, high blood pressure, and cancer, amongst others.

We now know, the evidence is really clear, that lifestyle—which includes our diet—plays a really significant role in these diseases. As to heredity, we really understand now that any hereditary factors can really be mitigated and minimized by a healthy diet. In fact, this was really the focus of Dr. T. Colin Campbell's China Study that he documents in his book. This was a 27-year epidemiological study in which he concluded that chronic diseases can largely be prevented by eating a plant-based diet.

In addition to that, the World Health Organization in 2012 published a paper in which they called out the replacement of traditional plant-based diets with those of a substantial content of animal food as a key risk factor in the increase of chronic disease, worldwide. This is important to know because, worldwide, diseases related to diet have continued to increase, and these increases are really being felt in developing countries.

The World Health Organization has said that by 2020, the vast majority of deaths from chronic diseases will be in these developing countries. We're on a trend, worldwide, that does not look good. All the studies we have indicate that this can be mitigated and prevented by eating a plant-based diet.

Bussineau: So, a plant-based diet certainly has some advantages. How is it protective? How does it protect us from these kinds of diseases? Do we know?

Morgado: Yes, we do know at this point. First, the understanding that one of the key driving forces behind chronic disease is inflammation in the body, and plant-based diets are anti-inflammatory. So, plant-based diets inherently counteract the effects of inflammation, which lead to chronic disease.

When you eat plants, you're not taking in any cholesterol at all—plants do not contain cholesterol; only animal foods contain cholesterol. You're taking in either low or no saturated fat—the only exception is coconut and palm oils. But, it's interesting because these plant-based saturated fats also act differently in the body than animal-based saturated fat. The studies now indicate that they don't have those harmful effects on cardiovascular health, that's an important thing to note. Just keep your intake moderate.

Probably one of the things that most people do realize is that plant foods are high in fiber. Fiber in the body removes waste and it regulates our blood sugar. Both of these have an anti-inflammatory effect.

Plant foods are high in antioxidants and contain phytonutrients. Phyto—the prefix "phyto" means "plant"—these are nutrients that can only be found in plants, they can't be found in animal foods. For example, when we look at the bright colors of plant foods—we think about the deep purple of an eggplant or blueberries, the bright red that we see in tomatoes and watermelon, the bright orange in carrots and squash, the greens from kale and broccoli—very beautiful, intense colors. That's really indicative of the phytonutrients and anti-oxidants that a plant has. The plants actually produce these things as a way to protect themselves from insects and diseases that plants can catch.

Bussineau: That's really interesting!

Morgado: Yeah! It's really interesting when you consider the fact that this is the plant's defense mechanism and that defense mechanism works equally well in our bodies when we take those things in.

Another thing about plant food is that non-processed, starchy foods actually help feed good intestinal bacteria. Many people today know about the importance of probiotics; that gets talked about a lot. The fact that our intestines have both good and bad bacteria and we need these good bacteria in order to be healthy and have a well-functioning digestive system.

There are foods that we can eat that are called pre-biotics that actually help provide the fuel or the food for those good bacteria. These non-processed, starchy foods we get from plants are one of the best sources of that type of fuel to feed good intestinal bacteria.

All of these things combined together provide us with a diet that really decreases, to the greatest extent possible, inflammation and oxidation in our body. Just the fact that we have a metabolism and we digest food and we are mammals that get up and move around—we walk and we engage in a lot of activity, and so on and so forth—we have some degree of oxidation and inflammation that just happens because we're mammals and that's the way our bodies work.

But, the plant foods really decrease, to the greatest extent possible, that inflammation and that oxidation. Whereas, animal foods are really the fuel for that inflammation and that oxidation. That's really the difference between the two of them and why a plant-based diet can really mitigate and decrease risk for chronic disease.

Bussineau: Thank you, Sherry. I really appreciate you spending some time with me today. I think that understanding protein and calcium better and the fact that we need to take B12—are very important for all of us to understand. Even those of us who have been vegan continue to learn and, I've learned quite a few things from our conversation.

Is there anything else in wrapping up our conversation that you would like to tell us about eating a plant-based diet?

Morgado: One of the things that I really encourage people to do is to educate themselves. There's so much information available out there now. It's good, scientifically based information. I know that people don't want to hear just anecdotal information, they want to be able to read the science. I'm just so pleased that, in the society we live in today, we have a number of registered dieticians and nutritionists who themselves are vegan, and have been for a number of years. They've written a number of really excellent books about the science of nutrition, about plant-based nutrition, and what it takes to be a healthy vegan.

I'm just going to mention a few of these, this is not by any means a comprehensive list. These are resources I myself have used and continue to use. There's a book called _Vegan for Life_ by Jack Norris and Virginia Messina--they're both registered dieticians—and this one is a really user-friendly book. It's easy to read and easy to understand. It's a nice introduction for folks if they've either not been exposed to a plant-based diet before or they just want to refresh their knowledge about some of these issues.

Something that is a little more comprehensive is a book called _Becoming Vegan_ and this was written by Brenda Davis and Vesanto Melina, again, both registered dieticians. There's actually two versions of this book, there's an express edition and a comprehensive edition. The express edition is for the average person that just needs a concise explanation of the science behind a plant-based diet. The comprehensive edition is for nutritionists. Again, two versions of that one—both excellent books.

A couple of other books that I've used: I think this one is very important, there's a book called _Never Too Late to Go Vegan_ and it was written by some really well-known vegan activists: Carol J. Adams, Patti Breitman, and Virginia Messina—who I mentioned earlier, who's a registered dietician. This book really focuses on what you need to know if you're over the age of 50 if you're looking to adopt and thrive on a plant-based diet.

I think as more and more people find out the truth about how animals are treated when they're raised for food, they find out the truth about factory farms, and they find out more about the health benefits of a plant-based diet, more people over the age of 50 are adopting this diet. I think it's important for them to have information that can reassure them. As we're entering our middle-aged years, our senior years, we can still be healthy on this type of a diet and it also addresses our special issues that we have as we age and what people's concerns might be. So that's a great resource.

Finally, another book called <u>Vegan for Her</u>, again, written by Virginia Messina. This is a book obviously focused toward women. It focuses on women's unique issues, including: hormones, fertility, pregnancy, breastfeeding, aging, menopause, things like breast cancer and strong bones. It's a very positive and affirming book that I recommend to all women that are following this type of a diet or considering it.

I just encourage people to read and become more familiar with these issues. You're just going to find a wealth of information in any of those books.

Bussineau: Wonderful, Sherry. We, as a general public, need to know more about these issues. It's in all our best interest not only our own personal health but also the health of our families, communities, and the world at large.

I appreciate you spending time with me today and I look forward to speaking to you again in the near future. Thank you, Sherry.

Morgado: Thank you so much, John. It's been an absolute pleasure and a real honor. Thank you so much for helping to get this information out to the public and to those that are practitioners, in particular.

Appendix B: Interview with T. Colin Campbell

Bussineau: My first question is relates to *The China Study* and *Whole: Rethinking the Science of Nutrition,* both of which document the relationship between food and cancer and other kinds of so-called Western diseases. I was wondering if you could sum up the effect of animal foods on the potential of getting cancer at the initiation stage. You write about the various stages of cancer in both books; could you speak about this further?

Dr. Campbell: Right, and, well, in research we sort of use that so-called model for investigating things and we describe cancer in three phases. It's more for the convenience of the research; it just has us understanding that way. But in any case, of those three stages, I started to look for mechanisms to account for this unusual protein effect. And on the first stage, initiation, we found what now I regard, four different mechanisms, so to speak, it might account for. Not knowing, of course, at the end of that work which one was the really significant mechanism. The idea that there are four, sort of all operating simultaneously, was intriguing. One had to do with the high-protein diet increase in the transport of the carcinogen into the cell. It was sort of an indirect operation, nevertheless, that's what we saw. Secondly, when a carcinogen goes into a cell, it gets metabolized through a more active product. And the enzyme responsible for that has a name, mixed function oxidase. That enzyme can speed up or slow down reactions, as whole enzymes do; that's their function, to speed up or slow down reactions. In this particular case, the high protein diet increased the amount of enzyme there, so that sped up the reaction. The second thing it did is change the conformation of the enzyme and that means that it could change the efficiency with which the enzyme catalyzes that reaction. So again it was a high-protein diet increasing the likelihood of the reactive product being formed. So then we looked at the ultimate end point of that first stage, and that is for this reactive product to bind to the DNA. And we measured that and sure enough, the amount of the carcinogen binded to the DNA really tightly, covalent we say in chemistry, was increased. And it was dose dependent with the protein, the higher the protein the more it was bound to the DNA. *So what that really meant was that the high-protein diet was increasing the ability of the carcinogen to increase mutations, which is the first step in cancer.* So we had in a sense four mechanisms, not really knowing at that point, though, which one is significant, or so-called rate limiting, as we say.

So then we turned our attention to the second stage and there we started learning some really interesting things. You know the difference between the first stage, second stage is a vague boundary, but in any case, the first thing we found—and this was a little bit later, actually—but the first thing we learned is that most of the carcinogens that bind to our DNA and initiate mutations, that's a process that goes on all the time in our bodies and goes on for a lifetime. Nature has figured out a way to deal with that and basically repair that damage, and that's called DNA repair. This is a normal thing, this goes on all the time, but in this case, the high-protein diet actually compromised the ability of that protective mechanism, which is really kind of strange, and then once the cells are mutated and they start becoming infant cancer cells, we might call them, then they begin to divide and they are recognized as being cancer-like, and that's where the body again steps in and has a new system to deal with that it, and it produces so-called killer cells, which are designed as the name implies, to go about killing these cancer cells. But it turned out that mechanism, which is there all the time, is compromised by high-protein diets, too. And then we started doing some other things. When I counted up at the end of these years, ten I guess we had, of these mechanisms, it finally got to the point after 12, 13, 14 years of starting this work, it was almost as if we were going nowhere because they couldn't identify the specific mechanism. By the way, that kind of question is usually asked by people in medicine, around medical research. Especially in drug companies, because if you can identify the connection between the cause and effect, and the effect is not what you want, you can determine which is the principal step in the mechanism, and then you might be able to make a drug. That's the basis of the entire industry, to be honest about it. It's a very profound assumption and understanding, actually. And in this case, I had begun thinking there is no such thing as a single mechanism, and even if we invented a drug to stop one of these mechanisms, the rest of them are still there. So the whole idea of trying to develop a drug to try to block stuff like this is still kind of foolish or silly, and I just found that concept, that argument, that idea to be very profound.

Bussineau: So a WFPB diet has a positive effect on cancer, giving our bodies the ability to fight the disease at various stages in the process. Is the same true for other ailments like autoimmune diseases, diabetes, and heart disease? Is there research that points to that?

Dr. Campbell: Yes. That's a big question, a very important question, but from my review of the literature, even though we didn't look specifically at those kinds of things, I am very confident that that is a very accurate statement and that in turn defines what nutrition really is. Which of course is very different from what we generally assumed. We can't just assume that each nutrient has its function and so therefore we need to decide how much to consume and what level may cause problems and so on and so forth. I taught that for many years. I taught the upper class course in Nutritional Biochemistry at Cornell for many years, so at the beginning of my career, that's what we did. We talked about those kind of details. The details are interesting and important in order to gain a better insight into the larger picture, but they are not enough and what you just said, you're right on point.

Bussineau: So I was curious, I've read *The China Study,* about four times and I give it to a lot of people to read including my primary care physician recently. I took in a stack of four books to my annual physical and my doctor asked which one I would suggest he read if he agreed to read one? I told him, *The China Study*. He asked, "How old is this book?" and I told him that *The China Study* was published in 2006 and he asked me if the findings were still valid and I responded, "Yes." How would you have responded to that particular question?

Dr. Campbell: Well, first of all, it was 2005 when it first came out in paperback. It was the same book. Then the hard cover came out in 2006. Amazon, the site lists 2006, when it really should be 2005. In any case, you are correct. As a matter of fact, as we wrote that and published it in 2005, what I see is mountains of additional evidence supporting that idea. I am absolutely convinced, I am confident, we shouldn't say this in science, I am absolutely confident that this will last for all time. It cannot be denied. This is the way nutrition works. It works in a very holistic way.

Bussineau: Has anyone ever duplicated the liver cancer experiments that you did early on in rats?

Dr. Campbell: Yes, there was a group in Thailand who did it sort of simplistically, but they did enough to prove it out. It was consistent with what was done in India, which was a very simple study that was published at the time. They also did it at UCLA School of Medicine. That was probably a little better, but beyond those two other places, I'm not aware of anyone. It's dangerous territory to get into, I tell you. I've learned that in spades.

Bussineau: How so? Politically dangerous?

Dr. Campbell: Yes, well, politically dangerous for certain, but also in protecting one's reputation. The whole idea that there are several things that I ended up doing that are both very productive in a sense, but also engendered some really serious criticism at times because people really didn't want to think this way. To say that protein, which is really one of the most revered of all nutrients in a way, to say that that actually increases cancer and that protein from animals is what does it. Man, that's pretty provocative idea.

Bussineau: I'm happy to say I believe it's gaining a great foothold lately (the acceptance of the idea).

Dr. Campbell: We've gone on, as you know, I went on to sort of add more content to the idea that protein did what it does. Namely, when we are consuming animal-based protein, what's happening there, is not only are we adding something to the diet in a sense that is multimechanistic and is multicausal for many different outcomes—we are not only doing that, but when we do that, it comes in the form of animal food, as you know. And considering calorie intake to be a zero-sum game, essentially, the more animal food we put in our diet, the less plant food we are going to consume. And that's a big deal.

Bussineau: Going along with that type of question. What kind of studies should we be doing today to further the document and support the findings in _The China Study_ and _Whole_?

Dr. Campbell: That's a good question, too. I can name a number of things, some of which are kind of reductionist, but I would suggest they are worth doing because it kind of fills in the gaps on the holistic idea, you say it that way. It turns out that the ability to be able to do the right kind of research and the research that needs to be done, you know a more holistic kind of study, it's very difficult because science was not founded on that idea. It is always focused on testing one thing at a time. It comes out of the drug industry, basically. And they try to apply that to nutrition as well. It's not appropriate. So, it means testing the whole diet. The more you get into that, then a lot of researchers and clinicians—of course clinicians don't have any training in nutrition—but the more we get into that kind of discussion, they say, "Well, that's really not worth it, which mechanism are you talking about, which nutrient are you talking about?" I had to face that crazy question many times and I would say, "It's not about one thing." I was on several committees reviewing which applications (for research) should get funded and which ones should not for the National Cancer Institute and American Cancer Society and so forth. I was very active in that area. What my colleagues would tend to say when someone came around with an idea like that, "Oh, it's a fishing expedition" or "It's a shotgun approach." These were the typical words used. So to answer your question, what type of things need to be done, we need to test the whole-food plant-based diet and understand and recognize that it has infinite kinds of food combinations in there; but just as a collection of different kinds of foods, correcting a collection of different responses. That's just how nutrition works. It just works this way. And we can't go in and try to study it without investigating that, without having that in mind. I think testing this on cancer patients or people with autoimmune disease may be by far and away the most significant thing to do. It hasn't been done very much because, as I said, the people who are making these decisions and the people who are generating the funds or getting the funds to do it, they are thinking that there must be a reductionist mode, so this kind of stuff doesn't get done. I am actually involved in organizing such a study right now. It sounds like a fair bit of money, but it's not. It's only $6 million, which is peanuts, it's pocket change if we're doing the type of study that needs to be done. But I can tell you that the cost, I don't know if you know this or not, but the cost in the case of cancer, of developing the chemotherapy agent when it gets to market, the average cost of that, and this is 2010 figures, so I'm sure it's higher than what I'm going to tell you, it's between $1.2 and $1.3 billion dollars, and furthermore they don't work. So that raises some huge questions here. So we've got to find a way to break that glass ceiling.

Bussineau: In your experience, have you seen that a WFPB diet is helpful in terms of breast cancer, or are there certain cancers that respond better based on your knowledge?

Dr. Campbell: Yeah, I mean, just because we can't do the study that needs to be done, we can rely to some extent on other types of evidence. There is one paper that is published in a period journal and all that was on melanoma, and this was done by an organization that doesn't have a very good reputation, but it was published in professional literature. Because people weren't sure, it was in collaboration with the University of San Diego Medical Center. But taking melanoma patients, melanoma is a very serious form of cancer as you know, and they just gave them mostly fruits and vegetables and grains and stuff like that, and they did a couple of other things, too, but they got really quite remarkable results. Now that was published. And then there are some claims out there, very provocative claims... [but one doctor I know] now has like 70 cancer patients, and they are doing well because he got his hands on our book and started getting patients to do that, and so we can make those kind of claims. From my perspective, if that's the evidence for some of the things they say, it's really based on science, it's based on my interpretation of the science. I have been quite deeply in this field for quite a long time, and so drawing from a variety of different kinds of evidence, which many people wouldn't know unless they've been around as long as I have working in these professions.

Bussineau: The paleo diet has been popular for a few years. Why is it unhealthy?

Dr. Campbell: Well first off, people like to hear good things about their bad habits. That's the first thing to say, and I know the guy who basically organized that, a professor at Colorado State University, Loren Cordain. I debated him or supposedly debated him three times. I doubt he wants to do that anymore. He really is talking about a low-carb diet. And a low-carb diet means a diet designed around fat and protein. That's just ridiculous, just patently ridiculous, because as you compare populations of people over a lifetime, anybody on that kind of diet for a lifetime, they have a much higher risk of cancer, heart disease, and all the rest. And you can't take that diet, there is no way you can take that diet and get a group of people on it, which have a disease and then see their disease reverse. It's not been done. But we can do that with a WFPB diet. The Paleo diet is really a hoax. What they are doing is just selling an idea that's wrong, flat-out wrong, and I would say irresponsible.

There is another man that they drew on, some of his work published way back in the '70s or '80s, I guess, by the name of Boyd Eaton. He was at Emory University at the time, I think. Anyway, Boyd Eaton was actually observing the nutrient characteristics of wild animals compared to other kinds of animals. He came up with some very interesting ideas at that time. He was a good researcher and he had some good observations which he published. Everybody caught on because they thought wild animals were better than farm fed animals, that was one thing, and it led to the paleo diet. The other thing it gave justification to was that animal food was important. Well, Boyd Eaton is still around, and I knew him 30 years ago, I haven't been in touch with him. But just recently I was at a conference with him. He's really a wonderful good man, good scientist and all of that. He actually is coming over to our side, so the father of that movement is about to—I think he could be dropping a bomb on the whole movement. It's just a crazy idea that sells a lot of books.

Bussineau: For many years I have read that animal products tend to be very acidic in nature and that this is related to bone loss; however, there seems to be new data out that suggests that the calcium secreted in your urine is actually related to the calcium in our diet and not the calcium in our bones. Can you please comment on this?

Dr. Campbell: Well, it's related to the protein and the calcium in the diet, right. That just goes against other evidence, and there was a book, a publication from Yale School of Medicine 1992, and it was stated clearly that the higher the animal protein consumption, the higher the bone fracture rate. Which is representative of the process and there were some studies done back in the 1970s by a couple of friends of mine, showing the higher the calcium intake, the higher the bone fracture rate, comparing different societies, in both of those cases. So the protein it chiefly points to is dairy. So the higher the animal consumption, the higher the osteoporosis process. It sort of sounds reasonable to say that higher protein can lead to more calcium absorption and therefore it is a good idea. But in reality, that's not the way it works. You've got to look at the whole picture. It's part of the story. Like the person who first developed that was a specialist in radioisotopes and you have to go with a Professor at Cornell, friend of mine, that was 30 years ago. That was Bob Watson, he has passed away now. But people, sometimes they seize on something they saw in literature or something like that and try to make it into a big deal. And I don't take those things seriously. I am certainly open to exploring contradictions, that's not what people disagree, but I want to see data and unless they have data that is published that we can validate and is supported by other kinds of information, then I just don't accept those kinds of comments. The public is very open to, just desperately, wanting to hear something good about their bad habits. That's just the way it is.

Bussineau: Earlier this year, we were all reading about the new U.S. food pyramid and it seemed at one point in time that it was about to be adopted and we were going to get a better food pyramid, or at least one headed in the right direction. However, it seems that a lot of lobbyists for the meat and dairy interests came in and got it changed. For me this was reminiscent of the story you tell at the end of _The China Study_, and I am hopeful because at least there was a public discussion and perhaps there are some changes coming. Does that mean that we are getting better, at least in the science community, in that at least we are talking about better food pyramids?

Dr. Campbell: There is a little bit of truth in that. For example, the most recent report as of last year, mentioned the word "plant-based" in their document, and they never had done that before, so that sounds like a plus in some ways. They throw a lot of data in there to make it look fancy, but if you look more closely at that, they are not shifting gears hardly at all. As a matter of fact, I wrote a critique of that when it first came out. They wanted a comment, and I wrote a critique of it and it was picked up by an organization called the Congressional Blog. It's a publication, actually, and they published it. And basically, what I said in there is that we ought to trash that committee, get rid of this, because it is a committee of the USDA and the USDA—I was saying that before that the Secretary came out and put his stamp of disapproval on it. They have done this for years. I've known that process really well and know the people involved and been on those committees myself. And what they do is a very political kind of document. Very much subject to the whims of the livestock industry who control USDA, and they'll throw them a bone every now and then just to make it look good, but then the next time five years later on an update, they will ignore that. It's kind of a spinning wheel that yes, it is turning, but it's still the same.

Bussineau: What about medical doctors? Do you think that the medical doctors and the medical community are more open to a whole-foods plant-based diet?

Dr. Campbell: Yes, most of my lectures now, and I've done over 600 since the book came out, are to medical schools and medical venues. It started out a little slow in the beginning, not too much interest, more of a curiosity than anything. In more recent times, I've run into a number of physicians who are now changing their practice. It's really quite exciting. I gave a talk in 2014, in the fall of 2014, there was a project called the Plantricians Project;[372] they had a conference out in California, in San Diego. I was asked to speak. They had just organized at that time an annual award, which they gave to me, which was very nice. But it was quite exciting to see as there were about 600 doctors in the room and I got a standing ovation. It was really wild. I couldn't believe it. And, so there are people within the profession, they are very serious-minded people, obviously they went to medical school for that purpose. And they actually, as individuals, many of them are quite angry that they were never taught that. And now, that is an issue. Number one, they weren't taught it, and number two, they are not reimbursed for providing that kind of service. So the whole medical system is really quite locked up and it really has been for decades. Just keep this kind of nonsense out of the system. And that's the way that I look at it and that's the way that they want to keep it just that way because it's all about drugs and reduction science. So it just takes a big shift in attitude.

Bussineau: It's a big pendulum switch. The last time I heard you talk was at the Plant-based Support group here in Michigan, and Dr. Joel Kahn informed us just before introducing you that, "We have hit the 30% obesity mark in the United States and things seemed to not be getting better, but getting worse perhaps as far as obesity." We are all aware that there's a lot of suffering that goes on due to obesity and all of the diseases that are correlated with it but very happy and felt a renewed sense of hope after seeing the movie *Pure Plant Nation.* What do you think is the best way to approach this whole pendulum switch; political community, scientific community, medical community, or grass roots? Is there a certain best way to approach it?

Dr. Campbell: In a very general sense, I think it has to be from a bottom-up approach, because going from top down, it is very, very difficult and I have worked at the top for a long time, being on expert panels, giving testimony to Congressional Committees and stuff like this. I know the people involved and I know the strengths they have. The elected officials, for example in the government, are elected thanks to the Citizens United decision in part, but they are elected because of money and there's nobody putting money in their elections that's going to favor an idea like this. Elected officials, their hands are tied. I meet with them personally and they say, "Oh that's wonderful, that's so nice." But they won't do a thing when they go back to sit at their desk. So of course any of the other people in government, like at the NASA level, they are working for elected officials, of course, and they keep their mouths shut, too. They can't say anything too freely. So the system is pretty tough coming from the top down, and so that's why I say it needs to come from the bottom up. It's much better and I think Nelson's [Campbell] ideas with the pods will create some momentum. There's different things you can do at the local level. Doing what you're doing right now and just interviewing, just getting it out there, is a good thing, because I think the internet, which wasn't out there 20 years ago, has a lot of power to convey information. Anything you can do along these lines to get a big audience, will be helpful. I have to say, also, that the power that exists from the corporate sector, it won't go away easily and it continues to respond to what the people get to know. So if people want to buy those types of products and services [plant-based foods], then the industry will change. So in many ways, I actually understand the position of industry. People think I'm very antagonistic of the industry. In some ways I am not, I just understand what they do but I don't like what they do. I don't like what they say, but people in corporate sector, they are basically looking out for the bottom line. The government, they are now being bought and sold, as I said, and I've seen this first hand for years in the committees. The nationalization of the industry with government and people. A lot of that combined activity, it's single voice almost, that happens virtually out of sight of the public. So, the industry and government are sort of arm-in-arm, working to keep things the way they are and, to me they serve the public with information, probably once a year and not too many of the media are freelance writers who actually get major stories published. I think the media in most cases is largely controlled, too. I'm actually writing a second edition of *The China Study* now and this is actually what I'm leading up to and why I am answering the question this way. We in _The China Study,_ did enumerate two different ideas about the sectors of our society and what role they play. You know, from medicine to science to government, whatever. This new edition, I have a new chapter in there, twice as big as any other chapter, and really, the one group who I have to say tried to take responsibility for this, for the problems, and they could be helpful with the solution—that's academia. That's my community, because academic scientists are generally regarded by the public as telling the truth, I guess. That's what we're supposed to do. There are a few that become very influential and offer their services to industry and they get on these panels, I've seen this, too. A lot of people are doing the right thing, but all it takes is just a few individuals to keep their hands on the throttle. And they come from academia and they get highly regarded in some ways because the public thinks that they are telling the truth, when unfortunately, is sometimes not the case. And I've seen this, too. Being in academia for all my career so I am telling in this chapter a few things which are going to cause some eyebrows to be raised.

Bussineau: I look forward to the new chapter.

Dr. Campbell: One of the things that's happened—and this is very discouraging—but in 1980 and these are data, not my data, but published elsewhere. In 1980, according to one poll, there was about 70 percent of all academics were in tenure track positions. You either had tenure or tenure-track positions where they had more freedom to speak as they want. Actually, it was probably higher than that, as when I was in grad school it was probably closer to 90% of all academics were in tenured positions.

Because if they couldn't get tenure, they had to leave, they had to go on to something else. However, the percent (tenured) has now dropped to like 25–30%. And that's a really very serious problem and it's something the public is not aware of. So, now the majority of academics, they are working, essentially, on contract. If they don't say and do the right things, and they don't get funding for research, if their interest is research. If they don't do research, they are not going to keep their position, they are not going to be promoted. This is something that happened over a 30- or 40-year period, and right now, academia in many ways has been destroyed. It's really very serious. If you could give some voice to that idea, that would be great. It's really an important problem. My colleagues in academia, my younger colleagues in academia, they can't say anything about this. They don't have free voice. It's one of the reasons I do speak out, one of the motivations I have because I've had tenure since 1973, a long time. When I came to Cornell, they gave me tenure when I came and they gave me freedom to speak my mind. I'm doing it now in part for the public because I just believe in telling the truth in the first place, but it also gives a voice to all those who would like to do the same and can't. We've got some big challenges, and it's gradually getting worse with time. Thanks to people like you and others who are using the internet these days, we can let the public know what is going on.

Bussineau: I will try to help communicate this issue. I have one more question, if you will. Based on your research and knowledge, does a whole-food plant-based diet improve one's health at any stage or age in life?

Dr. Campbell: Yes, that's an easy question to answer, from pregnancy, from infancy, and older. I've been told personal experiences from thousands of people. Additionally, we have done some of these short 1-week, 2-week immersion programs where you give people the food and it is just overwhelming, incredible results.

Bussineau: Thank you Dr. Campbell, I really appreciate your time and everything you are doing to help people and the world. I look forward to your new edition of _The China Study_ and I look forward to seeing you again.

Appendix C: Interview with Dr. Richard Oppenlander

Bussineau: Good afternoon Dr.Oppenlander, to get started I have a question about greenhouse gas, transportation, and manufacturing. Everyone seems to be aware of the greenhouse gas model for global warming that has been commonly accepted for many years. Al Gore and his movie *An Inconvenient Truth* were a big help in that; however, the movie focused almost exclusively on oil and fossil fuel usage. Can you explain to us why we can't just focus on reducing oil and gas usage in cars, trucks, and other transportation, and our level of fossil fuel use within manufacturing industries alone? Why won't that do it for us?

Dr.Oppenlander: Well, it won't absolutely do it for us because the levels of emissions from the agricultural sector, specifically animal agriculture, is high enough, that even if you eliminate fossil fuels entirely, take them completely out of the equation, just eliminate them today—we will still exceed the maximum amount of greenhouse gases that is considered our budget by 2050—just by animal agriculture and livestock alone.

And so, that's the largest concern that we have, that we need to address, but there is no emphasis [to do so] by any policy maker, especially the Conference of the Parties that are occurring, the conferences that are happening right now in Morocco. And it's taken 22 years just to address agriculture by itself. But animal agriculture is left off the table and needs to be addressed for two reasons:

> 1) Its projected. You can project the numbers quite nicely, that we will exceed our budget by

the year 2050 even if we stopped all greenhouse gases and fossil fuels today [related to transportation and industry].

2) The insidious mess of that is either we are not aware of that, the policy makers are not aware of it or the ones that are aware of it are failing to address it. So it not only becomes a mathematically need-to-be-addressed issue, in an insidious fashion it is staying off the table because nobody wants to talk about it. So it becomes even more of a problem.

Bussineau: I have recently taken a class called Eco-Sattva training with a group of other Buddhists around the world interested in making a difference in our world's environment. A highly prominent Western Buddhist teacher kicked off the session and discussed animal agriculture, and although he believes that it is important, he feels it needs to be changed but did not use the word "eliminated," and he quotes the 2014 EPA statistics as proof that keeping animals off our plates is only a small part of our problem—9% is what he quotes. And then he actually made a statement on his Facebook page that said a shift to vegan diet would certainly help emissions, but as long as fossil fuel is allowed to thrive, dietary changes will only make a dent. This doesn't seem correct based on all the research I have done, and it seems that 9% is exceptionally low. In addition, knowing who sits on EPA boards and committees, I am a bit skeptical of their numbers. Could you please shed light on this for us?

Dr.Oppenlander: Well, let's go over this. Great question; let me split that out for you a little bit.

First of all, the numbers. If you look at the numbers in the different sectors, for example, energy or electricity production with fossil fuel, combustion, things like that, as well as normal transportation and then industry, commercial, and residential, etc., much of animal agriculture-produced greenhouse gases are incorporated in a categorical overlap. In other words, some animal agriculture is tied up into those other numbers, in the electricity, transportation, commercial, and residential. So it's not just 9%, if you look at this across the board, nine percent is more related to livestock fermentation. There are categorization issues.

For instance, there is no accounting for the greenhouse gases emitted by our demand to eat fish. All the fuel, refrigeration processing, packaging, transportation, etc. is not accounted for that whatsoever in those figures. Additionally, the most recent United Nations calculations for all animal culture greenhouse gas emissions were at 14.5% not 9%. And so, it's not really 9% as you just mentioned.

But is it 14.5%? Or even 18%? Which is what they [U.N.] came out with in 2006, or is it 51% as Goodland and Anhang calculated? There are some other researchers that feel it is somewhere between 14.5 and 51%.

Most researchers and reputable gold standard organizations are not on board with the 51%. But there are a number of reasons for differences in the numbers from low to high, 14.5% to 51%. For instance, we just mentioned the lower figures; the 14.5% is without factoring in any of the greenhouse gases because of our demand to eat fish, but also, there is a significant concern for vast underreporting. In other words, across all types of animal products, there was possible underreporting that has occurred. And there was clear inaccurate use of the factor for global warming potential for methane, which they [U.N.] used 21 instead of 86. So the global warming potential for methane was really four times higher than the United Nations authors stated.

And in my mind, and in (the minds of) a number of others researchers, there is a potential bias, which you don't want to see among the authors of those United Nations reports. Because every one of them, especially the lead authors, are known consultants for the livestock industry. So, the incentive for minimizing, obscuring numbers, over-categorization, and under-reporting is very high. There is a bit of incentive at play here.

Another thing we need to understand is, regardless of where it is, whether it's 14.5% or likely higher, it's too much. And, we need to get anything that's producing any anthropogenic, human-induced, greenhouse gas emission, we need to get it to zero because, as you know, the predictions are that we need to look at this in an umbrella fashion, and this at the forefront of what we are talking about. Scientists are showing we need to stay at 1.5 degrees centigrade rise above pre-industrial times, not 2 degrees which what they originally thought. And we are already above 1 degree. So we are more than two-thirds of the way there, and it's accelerating. As you know, we also reached 407 ppm (parts per million) for CO_2 [in 2016], which is a new record.

Oceans are rising greater than they have before, all the precipitating factors are there. So most scientists believe that—for projecting, we need to keep it 1.5 degrees centigrade rise, and since we are beyond two-thirds of the way there, then we need to reduce our greenhouse gas emissions, not drastically, but by half in the next two years.

And then get it to zero by the year 2050. Well, OK again, going back to your question of comparing or at least reviewing fossil fuel use, greenhouse gases from fossil fuels, from gas and oil industry, and animal agriculture. Well, we know the greenhouse gases are accelerating, and the one that is accelerating the most is methane. It's actually on an upward curve, if you look at the latest Conference of the Parties curves, IPCC curves (International Panel on Climate Change). The single largest source of global methane is from raising livestock.

So, that's the reason I mentioned that we need to eliminate animals, our animal agriculture and animal products from our diet immediately, because we are on this timeline. We have to reduce our greenhouse emissions by half in the next two years. So the only way to do that is eliminating animal products, you can't just eliminate or reduce greenhouse gases from fossil fuel use; we just won't get there.

You can't just cut animal agriculture by eating less meat, because that is subjective; it's not going to get us there. And so the only way to do that is just to stop eating meat entirely. It is the easiest possible way to do this.

There are three generalized ways that we can reduce out ecology footprint—and that's really what we are talking about. I am going summarize all this in another way, by talking about our complete ecological footprint, of which climate change and greenhouse gases are just one. Just one component. And so I term the entire footprint as global depletion, essentially all those factors that affect our ecologic footprint that is creating this state of unsustainability that we are in right now. We are just focusing on climate change because it is front and center for most people. But—so to finish that about climate change, is that we need to also realize—is that not only does animal agriculture need to be at zero, but if you look at what's causing greenhouse gas emissions that we are concerned about—you can say there is three major ways to—or methods to get it down to zero.

One is looking at human global population. But we are not going to begin culling humans. We are not going to do that. And with the social implications, social or societal implications, of creating some type of global population control is not within our grasp in the next year or two.

The next method is to eliminate all fossil fuel use, which isn't going to happen, just because of the dynamics involved, anytime in the next couple of decades, probably.

The third method is just to stop all animal agriculture, and that is as easy as changing what's on your plate. I did it. I did it 40 years ago and I am not special. So If I can do it, anyone can do it.

Last thing to understand that, even if we cut all of greenhouse gases to zero, there are still implications of animal agriculture and our ecological footprint, because of all these other aspects of global depletion. In other words, you can take climate change and greenhouse gases completely out of the picture and say we have none. Well, we are still in an irreversible state; we are creating irreversibility, with a number of aspects of global depletion. Two of which are the conditions of our oceans with warming and acidification, but also just depletion of sea life.

It is predicted that by the year 2048 we are going to run out of all sea life in our oceans. Not necessarily complete extinctions but by collapsing of their systems. So that is irrespective of climate change. Not even in the picture. The Royal Economic Forum earlier this year, a highly reputable organization, stated that their number one concern for industry and society over the next decade is not climate change, it's fresh water scarcity. Not having enough fresh water. Climate change was number two on the list, well—animal agriculture is responsible for 29% use of all fresh water consumption in the world. And so if we are having this potential 40% shortage in fresh water availability by the year 2030, which it is predicted to be, how are we going to solve that without eliminating animal agriculture, which is now in terms of food production, is using the most water of any other sector in the agricultural industry?

And so the other aspects of global depletion need to be taken into consideration across the spectrum of our footprint, not just climate change. So I guess two ending comments would be the greenhouse gases produced by animal agriculture will continue rising, the more we consume animals, and if you take fossil fuels and eliminate those entirely from the picture we will still reach our maximum budget by the year 2050, just because of livestock. And reducing livestock consumption is subjective, is quite subjective, there is no metric involved and given all the other aspects of global depletion, including climate change, we need—the person you mentioned that stated, we needed—simply eat less meat or go on a vegan diet won't solve some of the issues, well, it will solve, it is the largest single component that weaves its way through all aspects of our ecological footprint.

So if you eliminate it, you've also then created a reduction of your ecologic footprint across this entire span of all those life systems that support us on earth.

And we haven't even talked about biodiversity.

Just because of land use alone, livestock are responsible for using 45% of all the ice-free terrestrial land mass on earth. And grazing livestock, pastured livestock on land as well as producing crops that feed them, in conjunction with extractions of sea life out of our oceans are the two largest precipitating factors for loss of biodiversity and rapid rate of extinctions that we are seeing today, not fossil fuels. Climate change always needs to be remembered as an exasperator. It's a precipitator; it takes an existing situation and makes it worse.

Bussineau: Doug Boucher from the Union of Concerned Scientists had an issue with the Goodland and Anhang report that 51% of greenhouse gas is produced through animal agriculture, and he also had issue with the weighting factor for methane and counting respiration twice. Is the report that far off?

Dr.Oppenlander: The reports of the low end which are 14.5 %, or like you mentioned 9% by the United Nations. But in particular the 14.5%, which is more recent in-depth report and just came out a couple of years ago. In regard to the 51% by Goodland and Anhang, there are some holes in it. And you are right; I think he mentions what many of the detractors or the ones that were refuted that were concerned mostly about how respiration was counted. And I agree with that. So no one should be throwing out figures that are not accurate. We don't want to ever put ourselves in that position when you are talking about the health of our planet. You really want your facts extremely correct, and in this case I believe that their figure of 51% may not be accurate as well, but there are enough scientists that have looked at this. None that have created a documentation or published anything yet, but there is enough that have looked at this. But also know that the 14.5% isn't accurate. So it is somewhere in the middle.

And that's the best way to view it. Even if you just play back or review what I have already pointed out about greenhouse gases that were not accounted for and also the over categorization where greenhouse gases from the animal agricultural industry were then categorized into electricity, transportation, industry, commercial—which should have actually just been placed right back into animal agriculture.

But more important for me as I said, the amount, the amounts that they [UN and EPA] finally had calculated failed to use the correct Global Warming Potential for methane. And that is just a well-known fact. Goodland and Anhang did use the 86 GWP versus 21 (they used the correct factor).

Bussineau: Can you briefly explain how our food choices affect land, fresh water, and oceans?

Dr.Oppenlander: One thing about our oceans, to help summarize a little bit better, is to understand that there are a couple of different components of that equation. One is you can't really have a logical or a respectable discussion on the state of our oceans without factoring in land-based animal agriculture, because basically, it's land-based animal agriculture that we just talked about with the greenhouse gas emissions causing warming and acidification of our oceans, which is now irreversible in our lifetime.

It also causes nitrogen-flooded dead zones, right now there is over 550 of these areas that are devoid of life so. So you really need to know that land based animal agriculture needs to always be presented in the picture of discussions of the health of our oceans. The oceans are more acidic today than they have been in the previous 300 million years, and at a faster rate of acidification. And at that time, 95% of all marine species became extinct and since that time, scientists—projected that it took 30 million years for the oceans to recover. So we are in a very dire situation with our oceans from land-based animal agriculture and the warming and acidification caused by that. Irrespective of fossil fuel use. But it is still fishing, the third component that has the largest impact of all because, as I said a few minutes ago, you can take fossil fuels and greenhouse gas out of the equation and we are still predicted to be completely devoid of fish or collapsing of their systems by the year 2048.

Bussineau: Yes, we have close to 4 million fishing vessels out there, don't we?

Dr.Oppenlander: Five.

Bussineau: Five million?

Dr.Oppenlander: Five million vessels, and the difficulty is that there cannot be a distinction between commercial and recreational at this stage. All fishing now; most industries are terming this overfishing. With 5 million fishing vessels on our oceans, we have a situation with overfishing. And so the certified sustainable organizations that come front and center in the public, and also with various businesses, to appease us, to help us feel better, or even justify continued extractions and help us feel better about consumption of sea life, they are helping oceans become extinct. But it's by definition alone, since if you review the definition of sustainability by the Marine Stewardship Council, as well as the Monterrey Bay Aquarium Seafood Watch, to the principle leaders and Alfa seafood—or by seachoice.org which is the Canadian version of this, the definition is tied into three factors. And by their own definition it is impossible [to have sustainable fishing]. And I rarely use that word. Not improbable, it's impossible to label anything as sustainable, because the first factor is that there can be no negative effect on target fish, and today as we speak, 87% of all fish that have been assessed in our oceans are affected by overfishing and either depleted, overly targeted by depletion or they are on the verge of collapse.

Ninety to 95% of all large fish species, like halibut, tuna, swordfish, etc. are gone. They are at 4–5% of their original historic numbers. So the first factor is nonexistent, stating that there can be no negative effect on target fish because the target fish and a number of varied species are becoming depleted—under their watch.

The second factor is that there can be no negative effect on other species. And so there is no scientist in the world that will tell you that they know every single thing about the effect of any species on some other species in the oceans, because it is infinite. Biodiversity, the inner connection of biodiversity, in our oceans is infinite. By extracting target fish without having an idea of all those fish on both ends of the spectrum on the food web that it affects [we are affecting biodiversity].

They are also affecting biodiversity by the mechanisms of fishing. Any fishing mechanism today is destructive because it's killing. There is no one that can argue that killing is not destructive. It is ruining biodiversity and it is killing.

So, the methods are typically gill net, purse seine, trawling, trapping and long line, and they also use, poisons and explosives even though they are illegal. They are [poisons and explosives] on the rise because our oceans are not regulated and they can't be monitored.

And so, because of all those methods bio diversity is being lost up and down the food web. Just because of the target fish are becoming extinct; we start moving on to the next fish in line which creates a serial depletion. And there is this cascading effect on all other sea life species, so the second fact; there can be no negative effect on other species, can't exist. There is negative effect no matter what fish you are taking out of the ocean. You take one fish, you are affecting whatever that fish would eat and whatever fish would eat that fish. And so it is impossible to have no negative effect on other species.

The third factor that defines sustainability—or sustainable seafood with a label as being certified you will find in grocery stores—is that there has to be a method of accurate monitoring. Today less than 1% of all of our oceans are regulated. So it is impossible for that third factor to exist. If you have less than 1% of oceans regulated then you can't have a metric that measures the effects -- that monitors all of our oceans. So it's really preposterous to think that this sustainable seafood has created any type of following. If anybody just reviews that definition of sustainability. So, that's the issue at hand when you are talking about the effect we have on our food choices, on our oceans, both on land, as I mentioned and now in our oceans by sea life being destroyed.

Bussineau: Speaking of serial depletion and moving onto the next fish, you caught my attention in *Food Choice and Sustainability,* on this new fish, the Antarctic toothfish, Dissostichus mawsoni, which is being captured in the Ross Sea. Do we know any more about these fish? I know that we didn't, at the time of your writing, even know what a juvenile toothfish looked like? Is there any news on that?

Dr.Oppenlander: No. No scientist had even seen one at the time they were extracting 3,000 tons out of our oceans. And since that time, they have seen some juveniles, but as of today they do not know enough about their breeding patterns and their migration patterns to have an understanding enough to call them sustainable. Or even their full life span, which is quite long. But they do know that they are affecting their population. The difficulty is, it always is in the retrospect they will find out, that these fish they don't know enough about, they are extracting too many out of our ocean, out of that specific Ross Sea that we will become quite aware of it soon. So that is the issue with all of these species is that sort of in retrospect, we find out what we have done you know? We will end up fishing a species like cod, for instance, that most people know about. But there are many, many other: Halibut, New Zealand Hoakie, Orange Roughy, 17 species of salmon, a lot of pelagic fish, even Pollock, they all have an effect on other species. And we are not in a position to be able to determine that you can extract, for instance, 3 million tons of Alaskan Pollock out of our oceans and it won't affect other species up and down the food chain.

And so that's the issue at hand. We are extracting because of economics, because of our culture not sustainability, and that needs to change.

Bussineau: You mentioned pelagic fish, what are pelagic fish? I believe menhayden are perhaps a form of pelagic fish?

Dr.Oppenlander: Yes, that is a great question because typically we pay more attention to the large fish, the more predatory fish which are, and as I mentioned, many of them are less than 90–96% of their historic numbers. But pelagic fish, such as sardines, they are smaller fish that these larger fish feed on.

And then these pelagic fish also feed in the other direction on algae, plankton—and it's the plankton that comes into play. There is a balancing here, and I am really over simplifying it, but they have a balancing of everything on the far left of the food web, such as the smaller planktons or phytoplankton, and you also have a balance throughout the entire food web and chain to the larger more predatory fish, like tuna.

Pelagic fish are somewhere in the middle. So when you disrupt their systems, you are really disrupting both ends of the spectrum.

And most scientists were really not concerned about these, [and are] still not concerned about them to the point where they should be, so their populations have dropped substantially. The anchovy off the coast of Chili and menhayden off Chesapeake Bay are examples. A really good example for your audience would be sardines, because it is close to home. Most people identify, they know sardines, and also it is recent. So for instance in terms of a certified sustainable systems absolutely not working and how very little we know about the ecosystems in our oceans, we just know today that sardines are in serious trouble. Most people would say, "Well who cares about sardines?" But I just mentioned that they're in the middle of this food web, so we need to care very much about them.

Their population has dropped by 93%, in just the last 8 years.

Bussineau: Oh my, I didn't know that.

Dr.Oppenlander: Yes, especially off the coast of California where they are noticed because, they once were the most abundant fish in the California current, which spans from Alaska to Mexico. And most scientists predict that they are not going to recover in the next 30 years, if at all, from our actions of extractions. So losses were initially blamed beginning earlier this year, little bit into last year mostly, but into this year on the Warm Blob. You can Google Warm Blob; it's basically this area in the ocean, the Pacific ocean, off the coast of California that is maybe 2 degrees warmer than other areas of the ocean.

That consensus has gone away. The Warm Blob isn't there anymore, but they used to blame the Warm Blob on just about any type of population decrease of any species in our oceans off the coast of California. But now they know overfishing or fishing in general is a problem. And so we just continued fishing sardines until we lost 93% of their historic numbers. So they are at about 7% of what they used to be. And as I said, they likely won't recover in our lifetime.

So the issue is that the certified—this is a classic example this—not only did we allow them under their watch, under the Monterey Bay Aquarium Seafood Watch, and Marine Stewardship Councils (allowed them to) become nearly extinct, their systems are collapsing as we speak. But, then there is also this issue of how much catch, what is a sustainable yield, how they come up with what a number of catch, trying to quantify this, how much of a species can be caught, and so they have this term called "the maximum sustainable yield," and from that they derive the total allowable catch. Whether it's for a fleet or a single ship. Well, the difficulty is that, as I said before, scientists don't really know what that is. They just place a number on it because of the economic demands of the fishing industry. Then you find out afterwards that they had no idea what it was, so all these fish species are collapsing.

Well the same thing is happening with sardines. The difficulty is that not only are they collapsing, but there has been moratorium now on sardines—it's illegal to fish for sardines as of about a month ago at least [Sept 2016], off the coast of California spanning from Mexico to Alaska. As well as they have also put a moratorium on various times, such as, for instance, south of Puget Sound for a couple of different types of salmon, because they realize they had no idea that salmon were becoming extinct again and their species were down.

But getting back to sardines, the difficulty with this is that whenever scientific organizations—or governmental officials on behalf of scientific organizations—place a ban on fish because they realize that it is becoming extinct or their species is collapsing, there is also this issue of bykill. Or they call it bycatch.

For instance, I call it a bykill because that is exactly what they are doing. They are extracting all these additional fish, or sea life species, out of our oceans while in the process of trying to catch the targeted fish everyone is asking for. So with sardines, as a good example, is that they are still caught, even though there is a ban on extracting or catching sardines in our oceans off the coast of California. Sardines can still be caught as bykill. And so up to 50% of the total catch of any particular fish can be sardines.

It's absolutely absurd, what our scientific organizations are relating to our policy makers and then what our policy makers are then initiating with policies, because it's still going to cause a collapse of sardines. And this is just one example of many of how they manage this. In fact many people are up in arms and alarmed by seeing that there is more than 3,000 starving sea lion pups that were found stranded off the shores of California last year. And the reason they were was because the mothers were malnourished and undernourished and their favorite food is sardines. So that is just a very simplistic example of how our food habit choices from our oceans are affecting other sea life, other animals, and other species. And then how poorly we are managing this throughout sustainable, certified sustainable systems.

Bussineau: Thank you for that, I was hoping to hear that perhaps we were getting closer to some better definitions of sustainable sea life, but it sounds like we haven't moved very much at all.

Dr.Oppenlander: Well, we are moving in the wrong direction because of the economics, and no one really wants to step forward and, you know, confront that. But this last year and the last few months I have been making a strong statement about the facts behind the economic aspects of that. And I don't know if you have heard much about any of my most recent lectures, but I think it is very important to know, and I wish I knew this information a little bit more about this information when I wrote the first and second books. But you have to ask then, what's holding us back from just giving our oceans a complete rest?

There have been studies in the last year and a half to 2 years that have been released showing that historically it worked. Where you just give parts of an ocean a rest, and actually within 10, 20, 30, 40 years, depending on how devastated it was to begin with, the sea life eco systems come back.

Specifically, some of these we just mentioned won't come back in our lifetime. But number one is that we have studies now showing that coral reef systems and various marine reserves have come back; they have returned, just by having complete rest. There are, 3.4% of our oceans are placed in marine protected areas, but the reason I mentioned that only 1% are monitored and not 3.4% is because of all of those 3.4%, 90% of them still allow fishing. And so the managers and directors of those marine protect areas have admitted that in various documents that they are below their objectives. And so that is why I mentioned that it is—someone might try to correct me and say wait, 3.4% of our oceans are monitored in—marine protected reserves, but that's a false picture.

So anyway, getting back to the economic aspect is very important to know the global fishing subsidies in 2015, I don't have it for 2016 yet. But it was $35 billion, and just put that out there, annual revenues from fishing were $90 billion. $16 billion is from high seas or deep sea fishing. So $16 billion annually is where the revenues are from fishing. So that's the economic overview of fishing in our oceans, deep sea. Not even, not talking about the reef systems. Well, fish sequester greenhouse gases. In fact, not counting all the sea life in our reef systems, just looking at deep sea fish. They sequester up to two giga tons of greenhouse gas emissions per year which equates economically to $220 billion per year savings and costs in our efforts to battle global warming, because they sequester greenhouse gases.

So there is a clear argument for banning fishing on the high seas, completely banning. Not only to let them recover, but strictly from an economic standpoint, because fish are more valuable if left alone in our oceans as live climate change mitigating agents, rather than as food on our plates; to the tune of $220 billion versus $16 billion per year.

Bussineau: Getting the population to eat zero animal products is going to be difficult. Would it be in our best interests to look at a tax of any sort?

Dr.Oppenlander: Yes, of course, of course there would be, and I have advocated what I call an eco and health risk tax for probably 20 years now. And the issue is that we are in the other direction right now, it needs to be reversed. Globally, each year we are spending $486–500 billion dollars in subsidies by the OECD countries [Organisation for Economic Co-operation and Development] to subsidize and prop up animal agriculture.

Almost $500 billion, so we need to first of all, we need to transfer that to plant-based systems, which would obviously help our ecological footprint immensely. Then secondly, there needs to be incentivizing, but there also needs to be some sort of top-down approach like eco and health risk tax that you alluded to, and I think that every product should have its ecological footprint imbedded on the packaging and also reflect the cost.

For instance, there are two different taxes that could be blended, but even with health risk task you would calculate the risk to individual health and to society by consuming animal products and then you would place that cost into each product that is consumed. Similarly, you could with the ecology tax calculate the damage that it is doing to our environment, which is irreplaceable in many situations, so it would be very difficult to come up with an exact figure, because some of them are irreplaceable.

But basically, there needs to be some sort of taxation applied so it would raise the cost. I don't necessarily agree with *Meatonomics,* a book published a couple of years ago that stated the price of a Big Mac. If it had proper positioning of the cost to lour environment it would go from $4, $5, $6, or whatever it is to $11. Well, that's ridiculous. n some cases some of the rainforests that are being cut down, deforestation and some of the natural resources that we are taking from our planet, its irreversible in our lifetime and irreplaceable so it would be very difficult to create what the cost would be. But nevertheless, there should be a start and so, this could be all wrapped up into what is termed Natural Capital for Eco System Services. There have been a number of studies showing that our natural resources are producing, this is without the irreplaceability I'm talking about—there are $51–63 trillion per year that we are using out our natural resources, and most of that is at zero cost, so natural resources are typically free for most people today.

So we definitely need to put a price on those items, especially food items that are unnecessarily extracting resources, using resources in a tremendously inefficient way. Sometimes we can produce a hundred times more plant products in terms of pounds or protein or just from a food standpoint from plant-based systems, than animal products. So there has to be some sort of economic relativity applied at some point in time.

Bussineau: Thank you. Can you speak to two terms bantered about quite often: humane and sustainability? And are they related in any way?

Dr.Oppenlander: I pretty much place a lot of emphasis on definitions and when we are talking about definitions, sustainability—and the definition of sustainability—needs to be better positioned to include food choice, and I always talk about optimal sustainability. We need to be moving toward optimal sustainability other than the subjective, just what someone might use as the word "sustainable" to fit their own momentary wants.

So, similarly with "humane." First of all though, humane has nothing to do with sustainability.

The other thing we need to know about humane is that we need to apply it not just to farmed domestic animals slaughtered for us to consume, but also the imposition we are placing by way of our domesticated animals on wildlife and biodiversity, which we are losing at a rate of 10,000 times the background rate, which used to be two to four species going extinct per year and now it's been 1,000 and 10,000 times that much.

The principle factors involved in that, one of them we have talked quite a bit about, which is overfishing, which I just call fishing in our oceans, but also from land-based animal agriculture, and so it's not humane, I think, to damage family life and ecosystems and with wildlife, either. I don't think it is a humane way to live to affect wildlife across the board. But related strictly to domesticated animals, which are where most of our thoughts have this application of humaneness. There is no humane way to slaughter animals. Even grass-fed system and cage-free systems. They are not raising animals; they are raising animals on paper to be and in some cases to physically be more humane than completely in Concentrated Animal Feed Operations , but that doesn't mean that they are slaughtered humanely. In fact, the National Humane Slaughter Act does not allow, it doesn't have any jurisdiction over transporting or transferring animals from the farm and on the transport vehicles and then through into the slaughter chamber. There is no type of government regulation for those processes.

Bussineau: That's very sad.

Dr.Oppenlander: It is very sad. And one of the things about "humane," the word, and the term "humane" is that wherever I traveled throughout many, many countries, and just about every state in our country, that definition of humane has been created and now sort of qualified by one person. Whether you are talking about— and I am referring to any organization, any humane organization, certified humane organization in the world, whether it's through the USDA, American Grass Fed, Humane Association, FISS, Food Alliance, Humane Society, Animal Welfare association, all of them across the board, American Meat Institute, even in Australia and the UK, wherever you go—it's basically they rely on their definition. Somewhere along the way, if you look at the tree of the definition, which branch it came from, the central origination point came from Temple Grandin. And therefore if every humane-certified organization in the world relies on not a committee or not an organization, but one person who may have and who may be viewing those animals in some sort of distorted or skewed view, then that definition is grossly misrepresented through all of these different institutions. And that's the concern I have, because it is in fact.

And we've studied her research, works, DVDs, and teaching for meat handlers and animal handlers, and across the board and it is pretty sad, and this is not subjective. It's very objective because, as you know, I have been involved with animal rights now for over 40 years now. So when she states that a pig doesn't like darkness, it's not correct. It's incredibly false, and that is one small example. We have pigs that go into the dark all the time into their bedroom at night, because they don't have any fear. It's all about fear.

Anyway, it is a whole other topic that's really— it's sad that we do not place— because when it is all said and done at the end of the day, regardless of all the implications of the effect of animal agriculture on our own health, human health, society's health, or what we have been talking about, the environment health of our planet. It will still come down to the fact that we are slaughtering another being, another sentient being we are still taking that life with our own hands and deciding to slaughter, when it is unnecessary. We don't need to do that.

Bussineau: Thank you Dr. Oppenlander. Any new projects, books, or activities that we should be aware of?

Dr.Oppenlander: Well yeah, I really appreciate you asking that; there is a very exciting new project which, I don't know if you have had a chance to watch *Food Choices* yet? But you've probably seen *Cowspiracy?*

Bussineau: Yes, absolutely.

Dr.Oppenlander: OK, *Food Choices* is another movie. I have been very fortunate, very blessed, to be involved with out of the probably six or seven films over the last 2 years. Some of them are moving along quicker than others. Some of them are using quite a bit of my work. One of the films was just launched in, I think, 142 countries, is called *Food Choices,* which is another documentary. And so that is one your audience should be aware of and it's on Netflix now, which is very exciting.

Bussineau: OK, thank you, that is good to know.

Dr.Oppenlander: Yes and that was just launched on Netflix seven days ago [Nov. 3, 2016] and I was very fortunate to be a lead consultant for that film. And so it is not like *Cowspiracy* in the sense that it is not stark but in your face type of environmental film. But, it is more well rounded in the sense that it is one that you could present first then give someone *Cowspiracy* after that maybe. Like the very next night. Because they are both excellent films, and this one pretty much discusses or reveals the three prongs of the platform of animal agriculture, which is human health, environmental health, and more of an ethical view.

Another project that is stemming off of that is a nonprofit group called Inspire Awareness Now and also a website and Facebook page and a Twitter account that's called Comfortably Unaware, so your readers can keep up with a number of things that are occurring there. Because this landscape is changing quite a bit every day and we are the only website that I know of that is keeping up with it correctly.

Across all factors of animal agriculture and how it affects us. And so another project that is being combined through my Inspire Awareness Now nonprofit group and the *Food Choices* documentary film, there is going to be an online course on the environment.

Bussineau: That is exciting, please tell me more.

Dr.Oppenlander: Yes very exciting, and the certification—and it's going to be an academy, essentially, online and it is in the works right now, it should be launched in the next few weeks. Along with that we are having an Ambassador Program where we will take those individuals who would like to move it along further and essentially take my slide presentations as they are updated and use them in various arenas. For instance, if they want to do it just for their community, academic institutions, with business, policy makers, or internationally. They are going to be taking my slides and we are going to have an Ambassador Program where they can just move right through this argument and present it correctly. So that is very exciting.

Bussineau: Very, very nice. Thank you, I will publish links to all those resources in the back of the book.

Dr.Oppenlander: That would be great.

Bussineau: One last question perhaps, you have stated, we are all stake holders in global depletion and we all need to be involved in some way in solutions. Can you leave us with some actionable steps that we can take or should be considering? What can we do?

Dr.Oppenlander: Yes, well, I am going to let you know one. However, I am going to arrive at that end point in just a second. I would like to first tell you that to get to that point, we will all be faced with the difficulty in increasing awareness with those who want to continue perpetuating animal agriculture.

Along with my Academy and Ambassador Program, we are going to discuss those arguments that will be raised that we will see over the next 5–10 years as we try to move this along. Much of it is centered in the "Better Meat movement" that includes eating less meat and Meatless Mondays, Permaculture and Regenerative Agriculture, and Paul Hawkens is going to produce a draw down (on our effectiveness). He is very respected individual with this draw down in his very limited in scope and narrow-minded, and it's actually going to do more damage than good. Also we see the Savory Movement, holistic management and sequestration grazing, it's basically about eating grass,fed animals instead of factory,farmed. And so this whole argument of that, of moving from, this argument is only about factory-farmed and we will be moving to a grass-fed systems—needs to be dealt with swiftly, correctly, and in a positive fashion. Because it will just impede our evolution to a healthier, peaceful, and a more just planet.

And so, most of the think tanks and the panels I have been involved with are all making those mistakes. They are all over focusing on fossil fuels with climate change; they are over focusing on climate change and not global depletion.

They are overfocusing on that we can just eat less meat, as you began this interview talking about. Just eating less meat and maybe it's better meat. We have to understand that any type of meat has too high of an ecological footprint for the time lines that are in front of us. We only have very short windows for each aspect of global depletion. And therefore, the only way that we can create true sustainability and what I would term more optimal sustainability, which would be a form of regeneration and rejuvenation. Because we have lost so many different resources and lost so much, we need to start rejuvenating our planet and ourselves. And the only way we can go do that in the greatest fashion, quickest way possible, is by switching out our plates from any animal product whatsoever, is by just eliminating it completely today and go to plant-based systems. And then continue educating yourselves by going to various books. What you are doing is just phenomenal to hear about and it, will be another source, of course, and find various resources by going to our website and we will guide you. There are so many different wonderful sources for information today, but basically do this for yourself and then inspire others to do the same. Be a hero. You will be a hero for yourself, for your family, for your friends, for your community, and for our planet.

Bussineau: Thank you so much. This interview was both informative and inspirational.

Dr.Oppenlander: Well, I appreciate what you are doing and I really applaud your efforts.

Glossary

Ahimsa – a principle from Buddhist, Hindu, and Jain background that seeks to do no harm to any sentient being.

Analytical Meditation – a form of meditation practice based upon study, reflection, and logical inquiry. It is founded on reasons, arguments, and conclusions.

Anthropogenic – caused by humans and relating to or resulting from the influence of human beings on the environment. The Anthropocene denotes the geological age, where human activity is and been the dominant influence on the environment and the sixth great extinction.

Ascetic – a religious practitioner who makes great self-sacrifices and endures a lot of pain through the practice of various austerities to obtain enlightenment. These austerities can take the form of not sleeping, not eating, burning, and cutting oneself. The idea behind this is if they can endure severe self-discipline and abstention from all forms of indulgence, they will gain some sort of liberation. The Buddha went through a period of his life as a practicing ascetic and it is written that he only ate one grain of barley per day for a time. During this period he was traveling and practicing with five other ascetics, who later became his first disciples.

Atisha Dipamkara – (982-1055) A great Indian scholar who spent the last 17 years of his life in Tibet, conveying many significant teachings. He is celebrated for his short dissertation called the Light on the Path to Enlightenment, a concise route to enlightenment, which became the Lam Rim. The followers of Atisha became known as the Kadampa school.

Bodhisattva – a living being who has generated the commitment to attain enlightenment for the sake of all living beings. The term Bodhisattva refers to those on many levels: from those who have generated the aspiration to become enlightened for the first time to those who have actually entered the Bodhisattva path, which is developed through the ten stages (called bhumis) and culminates in enlightenment, the attainment of Buddhahood.

Buddhist Realms of Existence - In the Buddhist view of the universe there are six realms we can become reborn into: god, demi-god, human, animal, hungry ghost, and hell. Each have their own attributes.

Bycatch – the unintended and unwanted fish and other marine creatures caught during commercial fishing for a different species. One species is targeted but many species are caught. The unwanted fish are discarded.

Bykill – similar to bycatch. Bykill is discarded and wasted catch. They are the sea animals caught by accident in fishing gear, species that the commercial fishermen do not intend to catch. These can include marine mammals, sea turtles, sea birds, and sharks.

Carbon Dioxide – a colorless, odorless gas produced by burning carbon and organic compounds and by respiration. It is naturally present in air (about 0.03%) and is absorbed by plants in photosynthesis.

Carnism – from carnism.org: the invisible belief system, or ideology, that conditions people to eat certain animals. Carnism is essentially the opposite of veganism; "carn" means "flesh" or "of the flesh" and "ism" denotes a belief system. Most people view eating animals as a given, rather than a choice; in meat-eating cultures around the world people typically don't think about why they find the flesh of some animals disgusting and the flesh of other animals appetizing, or why they eat any animals at all.

Concentrated Animal Feeding Operation (CAFO) – agricultural enterprises where animals are kept and raised in confined situations. CAFOs congregate animals, feed, manure, and urine, dead animals, and production operations on a small land area. Feed is brought to the animals rather than the animals grazing or otherwise seeking feed in pastures, fields, or on rangeland. There are approximately 450,000 CAFOs in the United States.

Concentrated Meditation – called Shamatha or Samatha in Sanskrit and Zhi Nay in Tibetan. *Zhi* means "pacified, peace," and *nay* is "remains." So *zhi nay* is about pacifying all difficulties, obstacles and imbalances (wandering and sinking) within your mind and reaching, maintaining and remaining in a state of tranquility, mental calm. One can feel they are really getting somewhere when we can train our minds to stay on the object of meditation for a 20 minute timeframe without wandering off or sinking into drowsiness.

Dead Zone – a more common term for hypoxia, which refers to a reduced level of oxygen in the water. Less oxygen dissolved in the water is often referred to as a dead zone because most marine life either dies or, if mobile such as fish, leaves the area. Habitats that would normally be teeming with life become, essentially, biological deserts. Many physical, chemical, and biological factors combine to create dead zones, but nutrient pollution is primarily caused by humans. Excess from nutrients (from and supporting animal agriculture) that run off land or are piped as wastewater into rivers and coasts can stimulate an overgrowth of algae, which then sinks and decomposes in the water. The decomposition process consumes oxygen and depletes the supply available to healthy marine life.

Emptiness – "The quality of the relationality of everything or all things."[373] (This by Robert Thurman is the most simple and clear definition on emptiness that I have ever heard.)

Epigenetics – the investigation of changes in organisms caused by alteration of gene expression rather than change of the genetic DNA code itself.
whatisepigenetics.com/fundamentals/

Exsanguination – the action of draining an animal of blood.

Gill Net – a flat, vertically suspended net with mesh that allow the head of a fish to pass but entangle the gills upon withdrawal. Essentially, fish get trapped in it by their gills.

Global Warming Potential – Greenhouse gases (GHGs) warm the Earth by absorbing energy and slowing the rate at which the energy escapes to space; they act like a blanket insulating the Earth. Different GHGs can have different effects on the Earth's warming. Two key ways in which these gases differ from each other are their ability to absorb energy (their radiative efficiency) and how long they stay in the atmosphere (also known as their lifetime). The Global Warming Potential (GWP) was developed to allow comparisons of the global warming impacts of different gases, such as CO_2, methane, nitrous oxide, and chlorofluorocarbons.

Greenhouse Gas – gases that trap heat in the atmosphere.

Humane – showing compassion or benevolence. It is a term used animal industry marketing to ease the conscious of consumers. It it simply a label which is untrue since there is no way to compassionately kill a being who wants to live and clings to life with the last of their strength.

Klesha – mental states that cloud the mind and manifest in unwholesome actions, including states of mind such as anxiety, fear, anger, jealousy, desire, and depression.

Lagoon – man-made outdoor earthen basin filled with animal waste that undergoes anaerobic respiration as part of a system designed to manage and treat refuse created by Concentrated Animal Feeding Operations (CAFOs). Anaerobic lagoons are created from a manure slurry washed out from underneath the animal pens. Anaerobic lagoons have been shown to harbor and emit substances which can cause adverse environmental and health effects. These substances are emitted through gas emissions and lagoon overflow.

Lam Rim – literally translated as "stages of the path," a Tibetan Buddhist teaching form for presenting the stages in the complete path to enlightenment as taught by the Buddha.

Lankavatara Sutra – a sutra of Mahāyāna Buddhism which recounts a teaching primarily between the Buddha and a bodhisattva named Mahāmati.

Lojong – literally "mind training." Mind training tradition came to Tibet with Atisha who regarded these teachings as precious. They are instructions developing the mind of enlightenment and are marked by three qualities: transforming selfishness into concern for others, transforming adverse situations into advantages, and learning watch all phenomena as like illusions.

Long Line – method that involves setting out a large number of short lines carrying hooks attached to a longer main line at regular intervals. The short lines are suspended horizontally at a predetermined depth with the help of surface floats. Main lines can reach 90 miles in length and have several thousand hooks.

Mahayana – the so-called "great vehicle," as it transports all sentient beings to enlightenment or Buddhahood. It is distinguished from Theravada, which focuses on personal liberation. The basis of the Mahayana path is great compassion; and its aim, rather than personal nirvana, is to become a fully omniscient Buddha.

Meditation – The process of guiding, training, and transmuting the mind that leads one to more awareness and eventually an enlightened state of mind. The process of becoming thoroughly familiar with positive attitudes and accurate perspectives through both analytical investigation and single-pointed concentration.

Milarepa – (1040-1123) a Tibetan yogi who achieved Buddhahood in one lifetime. His biography is a an example of hardship undertaken in order to attain enlightenment. He was the student of Marpa and a vegetarian.

Nitrous Oxide – N_2O, known as "laughing gas," it is ranked third behind carbon dioxide and methane in contributing to global warming. It is regulated under the Kyoto Protocols. According to the EPA and Inter Governmental Panel on Climate Change (IPCC), this gas has a global warming potential that is 310 times more effective in trapping heat than carbon dioxide.

Purse Seine –a large wall of netting deployed around an entire area or school of fish. The seine has floats along the top line with a lead line threaded through rings along the bottom. Once a school of fish is located, a skiff encircles the school with the net. The lead line is then pulled in, "pursing" the net closed on the bottom, preventing fish from escaping by swimming downward. The catch is harvested by either hauling the net aboard or bringing it alongside the vessel. Purse seines can reach more than 6,500 ft (2,000 m) in length and 650 ft (200 m) in depth.

Sangha – a Buddhist community of monks, nuns, novices, and laity.

Sentient Being – a being who has feelings, wants, desires, who can experience pleasure and pain, and can suffer.

Shabkar Tsodruk Rangdrol (1781-1851) – a great Tibetan yogi who advocated for the ideals of vegetarianism.

Spent Cow – a dairy cow whose production has fallen below accepted levels of productivity and profitability. A dairy cow who cannot become pregnant again, whose milk dries up as she cannot give birth.

Standard American Diet – (SAD) a diet rich in animal protein at every meal. It is high in cholesterol, fat, and oil and low in fiber, vitamins, and micronutrients. It is associated with many disease states and obesity.

Sustainability – a condition based on a simple principle that everything we need for our survival and well-being depends, either directly or indirectly, on the earth and our environment. To pursue sustainability is to create and maintain the conditions under which humans and nature can exist in productive harmony to support present and future generations. The eating of meat, fish, dairy, and eggs is shown to unsustainable and is leading to the sixth great extinction and the global depletion we are witnessing.

Tantra – an esoteric system of beliefs and practices utilizing visualizing that developed in medieval India and practiced in Tibet after Buddhism was extinguished in India. It is also known and part of as Vajrayana Buddhism. Buddhist Tantras can be traced to at least the 7th century CE. Elements of Tantric Buddhism can be traced back to groups of wandering yogis called mahasiddhas (great adepts). The goal of tantric practice within the Vajrayana (and Mahayana) traditions is to become a fully awakened Buddha. Those on this path are termed Bodhisattvas.

Three Purity Rules – a mostly outdated and self-serving set of rules which is ethically not in line with the core teachings of the Buddha on basic morality. The three rules allow for the eating of animal flesh if animal was not seen to be killed, heard to be killed, or killed specifically for your meal. This is ludicrous in today's modern world, with 70 billion land animals and 2.7 trillion sea animals killed behind closed doors or at sea. Sadly, many Buddhists still hide behind these archaic rules for shelter.

Tonglen – a Tibetan term for giving and taking (or sending and receiving). It refers to a meditation practice found in Tibetan Buddhism. Tonglen is done to develop empathy, compassion, and our innate ability to be present for suffering, our own and others, including the animals (all sentient beings).

Trawling – a method of fishing that involves pulling a fishing net through the water behind a boat using a net called a trawl. Trawling's lack of selectivity is a huge issue and is depleting the ocean of sea life. Any sea life captured in the trawl dies, including both marketable and undesirable fish, and fish size both legal and illegal. Any part of the catch which cannot be used is considered bycatch, and killed accidentally by the trawling process.

Tsongkhapa – (1357-1419) a great fourteenth-century scholar and teacher who reformed the Kadampa tradition founded the Gelug branch of Tibetan Buddhism. He was a prolific author and finalized the work begun by Atisha, writing several Lamrims, the most well-known being the Great exposition on the Stages of the Path, Lamrim Chenmo. He is regarded as a full enlightened being.

Resources for Making the Transition

There are numerous resources for making the transition. Two organizations I am directly involved with and am a volunteer for are Dharma Voices for Animals (DVA) and Plant Based Nutrition Support Group (PBNSG). DVA is one of the only Buddhist groups seeking to create a conversation about the eating of animals and its association with dharma practice. PBNSG is a group bringing awareness to people in the Detroit Metropolitan area with workshops, support group meetings, cooking classes, and a wealth of medical advice.

Dharma Voices for Animals (DVA)

DVA is an organization providing a voice for the voiceless and championing the rights of non-human animals within the global Buddhist community. Within the past five years DVA has become an effective global Buddhist animal advocacy group. It is recognized as a Regional Center by the prestigious organization the World Fellowship of Buddhists, and has 2,000 members. DVA has 26 chapters located around the world—and is growing! Some of the members include acclaimed dharma teachers such as Jetsuma (Ven. Master) Tenzin Palmo, Bhante Gunaratana ("Bhante G.," author of the landmark book *Mindfulness In Plain English*), Ven. Geshe Phelgye, Tara Brach, and Guy Armstrong. DVA has created a widely acclaimed film entitled. This film features other esteemed teachers, such as Therevadan scholar, Bhikku Bodhi, and *A Plea for the Animals* author Matthieu Ricard, and has been translated into ten languages.

Some of the work DVA has done includes championing landmark animal rights legislation in the Buddhist country of Sri Lanka, opposing the government of Bhutan's plan to build slaughterhouses, staging the first-ever Asian Buddhist Animal Rights Conference in Seoul, South Korea, and working with the largest dharma center in the West in support of their significantly reducing the use of animal products. DVA encourages Buddhists to adopt vegetarian and especially vegan diets and offers at no-cost individual mentoring and classes in plant-based diets.

DVA encourages Buddhists and those open to the message of the Buddha to talk about and reflect on how animals get from where they are living to our plates. This has led to many Buddhists turning away from eating animals and using products tested on animals. Each of DVA's members regularly receives an e-newsletter. You can become a member at no cost and add your name in support of our work by filling out the short membership form at: dharmavoicesforanimals.org/join-dva/

Plant Based Nutrition Support Group (PBNSG)

The Plant Based Nutrition Support Group is a 501(c)(3) non-profit group with headquarters in metro Detroit, Michigan. PBNSG's mission is to prevent and reverse chronic diseases through education, teaching by example, and providing local support and community. PBNSG advocates lifestyle changes that will disrupt the cycle of epidemic chronic health conditions and have a long term impact on the health of our community. There has been steady growth since that first meeting in February 2014, and currently there are nearly 3,000 members with attendance of 200 to 600 people at monthly speaker events. PBNSG is a great organization which connects the community via online education materials and support services, speaker events, transition classes, small support groups, and outreach activities.

The PBNSG website is located at pbnsg.org, and you can also connect with the group on Facebook, Twitter, Instagram, and Pinterest, by which they provide ongoing audio or visual posts of evidence-based WFPB nutrition content that is also deemed positive, useful, and inviting for individuals new to these concepts. For additional reference, please see the following short video: vimeo.com/168870485

Notes

[1] Dalai Lama. Universe in a Single Atom: The Convergence of Science and Spirituality. Pages 24-25. Double Day/Random Book, 2005.

[2] Batchelor Stephen. After Buddhism: Rethinking the Dharma for a Secular Age. 2015. Yale University Press.

[3] The magic number. Holding warming under two degrees Celsius is the goal. But is it still attainable? washingtonpost.com/sf/national/2015/11/29/carbon/?utm_term=.176ad83431bf Accessed Feb 2016.

[4] Historic Paris Agreement on Climate Change. UN Climate Change Newsroom. newsroom.unfccc.int/unfccc-newsroom/finale-cop21/ Accessed Feb. 2016.

[5] The Cambridge Declaration on Consciousness fcmconference.org/img/CambridgeDeclarationOnConsciousness.pdf Accessed August 2014.

[6] io9.gizmodo.com/5937356/prominent-scientists-sign-declaration-that-animals-have-conscious-awareness-just-like-us Accessed August 2014.

[7] psychologytoday.com/blog/animal-emotions/201208/scientists-conclude-nonhuman-animals-are-conscious-beings Accessed August 2014.

[8] .news.cornell.edu/stories/2007/10/meeting-two-minds-carl-sagan-and-dalai-lama Accessed August 2014.

[9] robhogendoorn.nl/wp-content/uploads/2014/03/Transcript-Carl-Sagan-en-de-dalai-lama-Cornell-University-maart-1991.pdf Accessed August 2014.

[10] scribd.com/document/235349161/Transcript-Carl-Sagan-en-de-Dalai-Lama-Cornell-University-Maart-1991 Accessed August 2014.

[11] Nanamoli Thera, Carlo Gragnani, Bhikkhu Bodhi, M. O'C. Walshe, Hellmuth Hecker, N. K. G. Mendis, L.S. Dewaraja, Bhikkhu Khantipalo, Bhikkhu Sobin S. Namto, Heinz Bechert. 2012. Collected Wheel Publications Volume XVIII: Numbers 248 to 264. Buddhist Publication Society, Kandy, Sri Lanka.

[12] acc6.its.brooklyn.cuny.edu/~phalsall/texts/bud-ser.html Accessed August 2014.

[13] Jewel Heart Prayer Book. Jewelheart.org

[14] Campbell T. & Campbell T. (2006). *The China Study: The Most Comprehensive Study of Nutrition Ever Conducted And the Startling*

Implications for Diet, Weight Loss, And Long-term Health. Dallas, TX: Benbella Books, Inc.

[15] AMERICAN DIETETIC ASSOCIATION, JULY 2009. US National Library of Medicine National Institutes of Health
ncbi.nlm.nih.gov/pubmed/19562864

[16] The risks of not going meatless: From the Editors: Mayo Clinic Health Letter, March 2010
healthletter.mayoclinic.com/editorial/editorial.cfm/i/404/t/The%20r isks%20of%20not%20going%20meatless/

[17] ncbi.nlm.nih.gov/pubmed/27886704/

[18] Joel Fuhrman, Eat to Live (need a reference point)

[19] Fuhrman, Joel, M.D. 2003. Eat to Live. Little and Brown Company.

[20] huffingtonpost.com/kathy-freston/vegan-diet-cancer_b_2250052.html

[21] Ibid.

[22] Ibid.

[23] Campbell, The China Study, pages 49-67,

[24] biochemistry2.ucsf.edu/labs/blackburn/index.php?Itemid=3

[25] Kahn, Joel K., 2013, The Whole Heart Solution, page 24, Reader's Digest, White Plains, NY.

[26] Greger, Michael M.D. 2016. How Not To Die.

[27] pcrm.org/sites/default/files/pdfs/health/cancer/seminar/DrRuthM arlin_TheCancerProject.pdf

[28] pnas.org/content/105/24/8369.long

[29] Vegan strongman shoulders 550 kg — a record, perhaps — at vegetarian food fest; Toronto Star
thestar.com/news/gta/2013/09/08/vegan_strongman_shoulders _550_kg_a_record_perhaps_at_vegetarian_food_fest.html

[30] Vegan Strongman Patrick Baboumian Breaks His Own World Record!; Clearly Veg; clearlyveg.com/blog/2015/09/23/vegan-strongman-patrick-baboumian-breaks-his-own-world-record

Two new records for Strongman Patrik; Great Vegan Athletes;
greatveganathletes.com/content/two-new-records-strongman-patrik

Patrik Baboumian, vegan strongman; Great Vegan Athletes;
greatveganathletes.com/patrik-baboumian-vegan-strongman

Patrik Baboumian, World Record Strongman: My Strength Is My Compassion; Free From Harm; freefromharm.org/health-nutrition/patrik-baboumian-strength-is-compassion/

[31] richroll.com/blog/epic5-challenge/

triathlon.competitor.com/2010/05/news/five-days-five-ironmans-epic5-launches-on-may-5-on-kauai_9335 epic5.com/

[32] ironman.com/#axzz3wBQZJbLB
en.wikipedia.org/wiki/Ironman_Triathlon

[33] jasonplester.com/bio/

[34] hawaii247.com/2010/05/12/epic-lester-roll-finish-5-ironmans-on-5-islands/

[35] Fiona Oakes: 'Queen of the Extreme' redefines art of running; CNN; edition.cnn.com/2015/03/04/sport/fiona-oakes-extreme-marathon-runner/

Fiona Oakes vegan marathoner:

- greatveganathletes.com/fiona-oakes-vegan-marathon-runner
- greatveganathletes.com/content/fionas-records-are-official

greatveganathletes.com/content/mega-marathon-tour-queen-exreme-fiona

Fiona Oakes: The vegan 'Queen of the Extreme'; BBC; bbc.com/sport/athletics/32055097

American Vegan; americanvegan.org/Fiona.htm

Fiona Oakes; Forks Over Knives; forksoverknives.com/contributors/fiona-oakes/

[36] Venus Williams vegan diet:

- si.com/tennis/2015/11/08/ap-ten-wta-elite-open
- si.com/tennis/2015/11/09/wta-2015-rankings-highlights
- veganuary.com/people/venus-serena-williams/
- usatoday.com/story/sports/tennis/2013/01/14/australian-open-venus-williams/1832413/
- shape.com/celebrities/interviews/venus-williams-interview-thats-not-about-tennis

[37] Barny Du Plessis – Mr. Universe Goes Vegan; My Heathy Vegan; myhealthyvegan.com/barny-du-plessis-mr-universe-goes-vegan/

Vegan bodybuilder, 40, aims for Mr Universe title as he says meat-free diet has made him stronger than ever; Metro U.K.; metro.co.uk/2015/09/24/vegan-bodybuilder-40-aims-for-mr-universe-title-as-he-says-meat-free-diet-has-made-him-stronger-than-ever-5351168/

[38] gymmorris.com/

[39] Jim Morris youtube.com/watch?v=tUtv4slpm-U

[40] Nate Diaz beats Connor McGregor, Rise of the Vegan, accessed March 2016, riseofthevegan.com/blog/vegan-ufc-fighter-nate-diaz-beats-conor-mcgregor-in-shock-victory

[41] Maria Ines Pinto Sanchez, MD, Premysl Bercik MD. Epidemiology and burden of chronic constipation,

National Center for Biotechnology Information, U.S. National Library of Medicine, October 2011, ncbi.nlm.nih.gov/pmc/articles/PMC3206560/

[42] ncbi.nlm.nih.gov/pmc/articles/PMC3206560/

[43] mayoclinic.org/healthy-lifestyle/nutrition-and-healthy-eating/in-depth/fiber/art-20043983

[44] pcrm.org/health/cancer-resources/diet-cancer/nutrition/how-fiber-helps-protect-against-cancer

[45] Greger, Michael, M.D.; June 6th 2014; Nutrition Facts; Do Vegetarians Get Enough Protein? nutritionfacts.org/video/do-vegetarians-get-enough-protein/

[46] nutritionstudies.org/?gclid=CjwKEAiA7f-yBRDAgdv4jZ-78TwSJAA_WdMa--ix9_mN4lwsmRUM7tILYKfljocVXg9HkVgxC5ASzhoCuDDw_wcB

[47] benbellavegan.com/book/the-china-study/

[48] nutritionstudies.org/casein-consumption/ Accessed April 2015

[49] Links for more information about Dr. Fuhrman, and Eat to Livedrfuhrman.com/

Dr. Fuhrman's Blog
diseaseproof.com/

[50] pcrm.org/about/about/physicians-committee-30th-anniversary

[51] Link to Dr. Esselstyn's Book, Prevent and Reverse Heart Disease
amazon.com/gp/product/1583332723/ref=as_li_ss_tl?ie=UTF8&tag=heartattackpr-20&linkCode=as2&camp=217145&creative=399369&creativeASIN=1583332723

[52] Graham, Dr. Douglas N, The 80-1-10 Diet, page 15, Food and Sport Press, Key Largo, Florida

[53] Capps, Ashley. 9 Reasons Your Canine Teeth Don't Make You a Meat-Eater. September 17, 2013. Accessed March 2016
freefromharm.org/photo-galleries/9-reasons-your-canine-teeth-dont-make-you-a-meat-eater/

[54] users.rowan.edu/~holbrook/MLM.pdf
animaldiversity.org/collections/mammal_anatomy/kinds_of_teeth/
en.wikipedia.org/wiki/Dentition

[55] What is a Frugivore? en.wikipedia.org/wiki/Frugivore

[56] Dunn, Rob. Scientific American. July 23, 2012. Accessed March 2015. blogs.scientificamerican.com/guest-blog/human-ancestors-were-nearly-all-vegetarians/

[57] animalcorner.co.uk/animals/lion/

[58] catbehaviorassociates.com/why-do-cats-sleep-so-much/

[59] livescience.com/10579-theory-questions-sleep.html

[60] mnn.com/earth-matters/animals/stories/strange-and-surprising-facts-about-how-animals-sleep

[61] meatyourfuture.com/2015/09/herbivores-carnivores/

[62] petmd.com/cat/nutrition/evr_ct_cat_nutritional_needs_different

[63] Graham,Douglas. The 80/10/10 Diet. 2006. FoodnSport Press. Page 19.

[64] Northrup, Christiane, M.D. A Diet That Protects Against Osteoporosis. June 2010. Huffinton Post. huffingtonpost.com/christiane-northrup/osteoporosis-treatment-a_b_585528.html

[65] Felicetti, Marcus. How to Balance Your pH to Heal Your Body. Accessed May, 2014. September 24, 2012. mindbodygreen.com/0-6243/How-to-Balance-Your-pH-to-Heal-Your-Body.html

[66] Imatome-Yun, Naomi. April 16, 2015. Accessed May 2016. How Does Fat Affect Insulin Resistance and Diabetes? forksoverknives.com/fat-insulin-resistance-blood-sugar/

[67] Greger, Michael, M.D. February 4th 2015. What Causes Insulin Resistance? Prediabetes and type 2 diabetes are caused by a drop in insulin sensitivity blamed on intramyocellular lipid, the buildup of fat inside our muscle cells. nutritionfacts.org/video/What-Causes-Insulin-Resistance/

[68] Ochoa, Sofia Pineda, M.D. Are we omnivores, carnivores or herbivores? Meat Your Future, youtube.com/watch?v=Z4NsMiOMmCY

[69] Grossman, Dave Lt. Col. June 1, 2007. Greater Good The Science of a Meaningful Life greatergood.berkeley.edu/article/item/hope_on_the_battlefield#

[70] Grossman, Dave, Lieutenant Colonel. 1995. On Killing, The Psychological Cost of Learning to Kill in War and Society. Bay Back Books. Little, Brown and Company: Boston, New York and London.

[71] Peck, Morgen E. March 1, 2012. Accessed February 2016. Carnivores Make Low Estimates of Animal Minds. Scientific American. scientificamerican.com/article/the-carnivores-dilemma/

Herbert, Wray. February 12, 2014. Accessed February 2016. The Meat Paradox: How Carnivores Think About Dinner. Association for Psychological Science. psychologicalscience.org/index.php/news/were-only-human/the-meat-paradox-how-carnivores-think-about-dinner.html

Bekoff, Marc Ph.D. Aug 05, 2010. "Oh, I know animals suffer, but I love my steak": The self-serving resolution of the "meat paradox". psychologytoday.com/blog/animal-emotions/201008/oh-i-know-animals-suffer-i-love-my-steak-the-self-serving-resolution-the

[72] Yourofsky, Gary, Best Speech You'll Ever Hear, Altanta 2010, youtube.com/watch?v=es6U00LMmC4

[73] animalstudies.msu.edu/Slaughterhouses_and_Increased_Crime_Rates.pdf

[74] humanecologyreview.org/pastissues/her171/Fitzgerald.pdf

[75] booksandjournals.brillonline.com/content/journals/10.1163/15685306-12341380

[76] ncbi.nlm.nih.gov/pmc/articles/PMC4841092/

[77] advocacy.britannica.com/blog/advocacy/2013/03/creating-killers-human-tolls-of-slaughter/

[78] shellethics.com/law/studies-link-slaughterhouses-violent-crimes-increase/

[79] Batchelor, Stephen. Guide to the Bodhisattva's Way of Life, Shantideva. 1979: Library of Tibetan Works and Archives, Dharamsalla, Indraprastha Press (CBT) New Delhi.

[80] cdc.gov/obesity/data/adult.html

[81] cdc.gov/heartdisease/facts.htm

[82] cancer.org/research/cancerfactsstatistics/cancerfactsfigures2016/index
595,690 estimated for 2016

[83] diabetes.org/diabetes-basics/statistics/?referrer=google.com/

[84] Campbell, Colin T., PowerPoint slide presentation, March 5, 2014.

[85] Thoreau, Henry. Thoreau on Land: Nature's Canvas. Copyright 2001 by the Thoreau Society. Houghton Mifflin Company, New York, New York 10003.

[86] fao.org/newsroom/en/news/2006/1000448/index.html

[87] Accessed, June 10, 2014, fao.org/newsroom/en/news/2006/1000448/index.html

[88] IBID

[89] Thornton, Phillip, Mario Herrero, and Polly Ericksen. "Livestock and Climate Change." Livestock Exchange, no. 3 (2011). cgspace.cgiar.org/bitstream/handle/10568/10601/IssueBrief3.pdf

[90] USA Today, March 30, 2014. usatoday.com/story/weather/2014/03/30/climate-change-report-ipcc/7085937/

[91] National Geographic, page 35, July 2014, Five step plan to feed the world

[92] London Evening Standard, March 30, 2014. standard.co.uk/panewsfeeds/cut-out-meat-to-hit-emissions-aim-9230431.html

[93] Electric Cars Aren't Enough — Try Vegan for Earth Day. Accessed May 2014. huffingtonpost.com/tracy-reiman/electric-cars-arent-enoug_b_5187669.html

[94] awfw.org/factory-farms/

[95] ciwf.org.uk/media/3640540/ciwf_strategic_plan_20132017.pdf

[96] adaptt.org/killcounter.html

[97] 11 Convincing Reasons that Going Vegan Isn't Crazy. rd.com/slideshows/going-vegan/comment-page-2/#slideshow=slide6

[98] vegetarianstar.com/2014/04/21/christian-serratos-asks-electric-car-drivers-to-go-vegetarian-in-peta-ad/
wetpaint.com/christian-serratos-vegan-peta-encourages-825124/

[99] Eating Animals, page 58

[100] animalplanet.com/tv-shows/whale-wars/about-whaling/interviews-paul-watson.htm

[101] epa.gov/ghgemissions/overview-greenhouse-gases

[102] epa.gov/ghgemissions/understanding-global-warming-potentials

[103] thinkprogress.org/how-the-epa-and-new-york-times-are-getting-methane-all-wrong-eba3397ce9e5#.wg9dsup14

[104] climatewest.org/2014/07/02/time-for-epa-to-come-clean-on-methane/

[105] science.sciencemag.org/content/326/5953/716.figures-only

[106] coml.org/discoveries/trends/predatory_fish_decline Accessed June 2017.

[107] courthousenews.com/overfishing-claims-90-percent-predator-fish-caribbean-reefs/ Accessed September 2017.

[108] dailytarheel.com/article/2017/03/qa-with-biology-professor-john-bruno-on-decline-of-fish-in-coral-reefs Accessed September 2017.

[109] scientificamerican.com/article/predatory-fish-have-declined-by-two-thirds-in-the-20th-century/ Accessed June 2017.

[110] news.nationalgeographic.com/news/2006/11/061102-seafood-threat.html Accessed June 2017.

[111] ioos.noaa.gov/wp-content/uploads/2015/10/worm-et-al.pdf Accessed June 2017.

[112] spc.int/coastfish/Sections/Development/FDSPublications/FDSManuals/HLL/HLL2s.pdf Accessed June 2017.

[113] marine-conservation.org/what-we-do/program-areas/how-we-fish/destructive-fishing/ Accessed June 2017.

[114] Holy, Norman. Deserted Ocean: A Social History of Depletion. Page 110. 2009. AuthorHouse, Bloomington, IN.

[115] animalsaustralia.org/features/super-scary-super-trawlers.php Accessed June 2017.

[116] nmfs.noaa.gov/pr/interactions/gear/purseseine.htm Accessed June 2017.

[117] greenpeace.org/international/Global/international/publications/oceans/2013/Longline-Infographic.jpg

[118] safinacenter.org/2015/08/fishing-gear-101-longlines-the-snaggers/

[119] fao.org/fishery/fishtech/1010/en Accessed June 2017.

[120] Oppenlander, Richard. Food Choice and Sustainability. Page 129.

[121] ncbi.nlm.nih.gov/labs/articles/24331555/

[122] birdlife.org/worldwide/news/high-seas-heroes-saving-albatrosses-extinction-decade-success Accessed June 2017.

[123] nytimes.com/1996/11/05/science/long-line-fishing-seen-as-damaging-to-some-fish-and-to-the-albatross.html Accessed June 2017.

[124] pewtrusts.org/en/research-and-analysis/issue-briefs/2014/05/02/lets-find-a-better-way-to-catch-pacific-swordfish Accessed June 2017.

[125] worldwildlife.org/species/bluefin-tuna Accessed June 2017.

[126] safinacenter.org/2015/03/fishing-gear-101-gillnets-entanglers/ Accessed June 2017.

[127] nmfs.noaa.gov/pr/interactions/gear/gillnet.htm Accessed June 2017.

[128] peta.org/issues/animals-used-for-food/factory-farming/fish/commercial-fishing/ Accessed June 2017.

129

greenpeace.org/international/en/campaigns/oceans/seafood/understanding-the-problem/fisheries-problems-today/pelagic-gillnets/ Accessed June 2017.

130 fishcount.org.uk/fish-welfare-in-commercial-fishing/capture/gillnet Accessed June 2017.

131 oceanservice.noaa.gov/facts/pelagic.html Accessed June 2017.

132 ncbi.nlm.nih.gov/pmc/articles/PMC3306684/ Accessed June 2017.

133 eenews.net/greenwire/2017/03/27/stories/1060052131 Accessed June 2017.

134 usnews.com/news/best-states/california/articles/2017-04-10/pacific-sardine-fishery-closed-for-commercial-season Accessed June 2017.

135 businessinsider.com/sea-lion-pups-sick-dying-california-2016-3 Accessed June 2017.

136 latimes.com/science/sciencenow/la-sci-sn-starving-sea-lion-pups-20160301-story.html Accessed June 2017.

137 sacbee.com/opinion/op-ed/soapbox/article18430205.html Accessed June 2017.

138 motherboard.vice.com/en_us/article/climate-change-is-stranding-hundreds-of-dying-baby-sea-lions-in-california Accessed June 2017.

139 oceana.org/living-blue/sustainable-seafood-guide Accessed June 2017.

140 seafoodwatch.org/-/m/sfw/pdf/guides/mba-seafoodwatch-west-coast-guide.pdf?la=en Accessed June 2017.

141 epa.gov/ocean-acidification/effects-ocean-and-coastal-acidification-ecosystems Accessed June 2017.

142 pmel.noaa.gov/co2/story/What+is+Ocean+Acidification%3F Accessed June 2017.

143 climateinterpreter.org/content/effects-ocean-acidification-marine-food-chain Accessed June 2017.

144 usa.oceana.org/effects-ocean-acidification-marine-species-ecosystems Accessed June 2017.

145 ocean.nationalgeographic.com/ocean/explore/pristine-seas/critical-issues-ocean-acidification/ Accessed June 2017.

146 news.nationalgeographic.com/2017/04/great-barrier-reef-climate-change-coral-bleaching/ Accessed June 2017.

[147] theguardian.com/environment/2017/apr/10/great-barrier-reef-terminal-stage-australia-scientists-despair-latest-coral-bleaching-data Accessed June 2017.

[148] npr.org/sections/thetwo-way/2017/04/10/523254085/great-barrier-reef-hit-by-bleaching-for-the-second-year-in-a-row Accessed June 2017.

[149] forbes.com/sites/trevornace/2017/04/15/the-great-barrier-reef-is-its-final-terminal-stage/#1502bf783f2e Accessed June 2017.

[150] cnn.com/2017/04/10/asia/great-barrier-reef-coral-bleaching/index.html Accessed June 2017.

[151] nap.edu/read/12904/chapter/6#76 Accessed June 2017.

[152] fao.org/docrep/006/y4773e/y4773e05.htm Accessed June 2017.

[153] oceanhealthindex.org/methodology/components/habitat-destruction-intertidal Accessed June 2017.

[154] oceanservice.noaa.gov/facts/coral-overfishing.html Accessed June 2017.

[155] reefresilience.org/coral-reefs/stressors/local-stressors/overfishing-and-destructive-fishing-threats/ Accessed June 2017.

[156] ocean.nationalgeographic.com/ocean/critical-issues-marine-habitat-destruction/ Accessed June 2017.

[157] Accessed July 2014. farmanddairy.com/news/california-leads-u-s-milk-production-ohio-dairy-herd-numbers-drop/177273.html

[158] statista.com/statistics/194962/top-10-us-states-by-number-of-milk-cows/

[159] Accessed June 2014. ecowatch.com/2014/05/27/factory-farm-manure-management-cafos/

[160] wisconsinwatch.org/2015/11/nitrate-in-water-widespread-current-rules-no-match-for-it/

[161] Animal Factory, David Kirby, introduction.

[162] ncbi.nlm.nih.gov/pmc/articles/PMC1638204/

[163] Accessed July 2014. pewtrusts.org/~/media/legacy/uploadedfiles/peg/publications/report/PCIFAPFINALpdf.pdf

[164] Ibid.

[165] Accessed July 2014. sustainabletable.org/859/industrial-livestock-production

[166] Accessed July 2014. sustainabletable.org/859/industrial-livestock-production

167

nejm.org/doi/full/10.1056/NEJM199407213310304#t=articleBackground

168 Accessed July 2014. nrdc.org/water/pollution/ffarms.asp
169 Accessed July 2014. nrdc.org/water/pollution/ffarms.asp
170 Accessed August 2014.
oceanservice.noaa.gov/facts/deadzone.html
171 Accessed August 2014.
en.wikipedia.org/wiki/Dead_zone_(ecology)
172 Accessed August 2014.
teachoceanscience.net/teaching_resources/education_modules/
dead_zones/learn_about/
173 Accessed August 2014. scientificamerican.com/article/oceanic-
dead-zones-spread/
174 Accessed August 2014.
en.wikipedia.org/wiki/Dead_zone_(ecology)
175 Accessed August 2014. sfgate.com/green/article/Scientists-
alarmed-by-ocean-dead-zone-growth-3200041.php
176 cnn.com/2012/07/17/world/europe/dead-zone-baltic-oxygen/
177 epa.gov/ms-htf/northern-gulf-mexico-hypoxic-zone
178 Accessed August 2014. coastalscience.noaa.gov/news/coastal-
pollution/noaa-partners-issue-dead-zone-predictions-gulf-
mexico-chesapeake-bay/
179 Accessed August 2014.
books.google.com/books?id=6TNHAAAAYAAJ&q=Corn+needs+m
ore+nitrogen++than+many+other+plants&dq=Corn+needs+more+
nitrogen++than+many+other+plants&hl=en&sa=X&ved=0CD8Q6A
EwBGoVChMI3PG3g8X3xwIVxjY-Ch07igK6
books.google.com/books?id=sLr7AtqDDeYC&pg=PA147&dq=Corn+ne
eds+more+nitrogen++than+many+other+plants&hl=en&sa=X&ve
d=0CEMQ6AEwBWoVChMI3PG3g8X3xwIVxjY-
Ch07igK6#v=onepage&q=Corn%20needs%20more%20nitrogen%2
0%20than%20many%20other%20plants&f=false
books.google.com/books?id=LhAdAQAAMAAJ&q=Corn+needs+more
+nitrogen++than+many+other+plants&dq=Corn+needs+more+nit
rogen++than+many+other+plants&hl=en&sa=X&ved=0CFAQ6AE
wB2oVChMI3PG3g8X3xwIVxjY-Ch07igK6
books.google.com/books?id=LhAdAQAAMAAJ&q=Corn+needs+more
+nitrogen++than+many+other+plants&dq=Corn+needs+more+nit

rogen++than+many+other+plants&hl=en&sa=X&ved=0CFAQ6AE
wB2oVChMI3PG3g8X3xwIVxjY-Ch07igK6

[180] Accessed August 2014. scientificamerican.com/article/ocean-dead-zones/

[181] Accessed August 2014. scientificamerican.com/article/oceanic-dead-zones-spread/

[182] Accessed August 2014. scientificamerican.com/article/oceanic-dead-zones-spread/

[183] Accessed August 2014. organicconsumers.org/articles/article_19279.cfm

[184] Accessed August 2014. epa.gov/agriculture/ag101/cropmajor.html

[185] Accessed August 2014. organicconsumers.org/articles/article_19279.cfm Farm Animals Aren't Alone in Suffering Industrial Agriculture's Terrible Effects, By David Steele, The Canada Earthsaver, Fall 2009

[186] Accessed August 2014. earthsave.ca/newsletter

[187] Accessed August 2014. coastalscience.noaa.gov/news/coastal-pollution/national-harmful-algal-bloom-hypoxia-legislation-passes-congress/

[188] Accessed August 2014. coastalscience.noaa.gov/news/coastal-pollution/gliders-map-gulf-mexico-dead-zone/

[189] Accessed July 2014. latimes.com/opinion/readersreact/la-le-0720-sunday-water-drought-20140720-story.html

[190] Accessed July 2014. latimes.com/local/lanow/la-me-ln-drought-california-water-wasters-20140716-story.html

[191] nytimes.com/2015/04/02/us/california-imposes-first-ever-water-restrictions-to-deal-with-drought.html

[192] nytimes.com/2016/05/19/us/california-suspends-water-restrictions.html?_r=0

[193] washingtonpost.com/national/health-science/drought-hasnt-lifted-but-californias-water-restrictions-just-did/2016/05/28/bb555dec-22bd-11e6-8690-f14ca9de2972_story.html?utm_term=.409a3a26daab

[194] Accessed July 2014. curiosity.discovery.com/question/much-water-use-shower

[195] Accessed July 2014. bae.ncsu.edu/programs/extension/publicat/wqwm/he251.html

[196] Accessed July 2014. waterfootprint.org/Reports/Report49-WaterFootprintSoy.pdf

[197] First published in 2011 by Conari Press, an impring of Red Wheel/Weiser, LLC with offices at 500 Third Street, Suite 230, San Francisco, CA 94107 www.redwheelweiser.com Copyright 2001, 2011 by John Robbins. ISBN 978-1-57324-487-9. Page 236, The Food Revolution, 10 anniversary edition

[198] vegsource.com/articles/factoids.htm Accessed July 2014.

[199] bioscience.oxfordjournals.org/content/54/10/909.full

[200] www2.worldwater.org/data20082009/Table19.pdf

[201] waterfootprint.org/media/downloads/Mekonnen-Hoekstra-2012-WaterFootprintFarmAnimalProducts.pdf

[202] waterfootprint.org/en/

[203] environment.nationalgeographic.com/environment/freshwater/embedded-water/

[204] water.usgs.gov/edu/earthgwaquifer.html Accessed February 2017.

[205] blogs.ei.columbia.edu/2015/08/03/the-growing-groundwater-crisis/ National Geographic article. Accessed January 2017.

[206] water.usgs.gov/edu/gwdepletion.html Accessed February 2017.

[207] scientificamerican.com/article/the-ogallala-aquifer/ Accessed February 2017.

[208] modernfarmer.com/2015/07/ogallala-aquifer-depletion/ Accessed January 2017.

[209] nbcnews.com/news/us-news/last-drop-americas-breadbasket-faces-dire-water-crisis-n146836 Accessed January 2017.

[210] kansascity.com/news/local/article326058/High-Plains-Aquifer-will-be-69-percent-depleted-in-50-years-K-State-study-says.html Accessed December 2016.

[211] nbcnews.com/news/us-news/last-drop-americas-breadbasket-faces-dire-water-crisis-n146836 Accessed December 2016.

[212] washingtonpost.com/news/wonk/wp/2013/09/12/how-long-before-the-midwest-runs-out-of-water/?utm_term=.a185b8b9d90c Accessed December 2016.

[213] web.mit.edu/12.000/www/m2012/finalwebsite/ Accessed December 2016.

[214] modernfarmer.com/2015/07/ogallala-aquifer-depletion/ Accessed December 2016.

[215] news.nationalgeographic.com/news/2014/08/140819-groundwater-california-drought-aquifers-hidden-crisis/ Accessed December 2016.

[216] ers.usda.gov/topics/farm-practices-management/irrigation-water-use.aspx Accessed February 2017.

[217] ers.usda.gov/topics/farm-practices-management/irrigation-water-use/background.aspx Accessed February 2017.

[218] cspinet.org/new/200608011.html Accessed February 2017.

[219] motherjones.com/tom-philpott/2013/09/corn-and-beef-sucking-high-plains-dry Accessed February 2017.

[220] nationalgeographic.com/freshwater/freshwater-crisis.html Accessed January 2017.

[221] mercurynews.com/2014/03/29/california-drought-san-joaquin-valley-sinking-as-farmers-race-to-tap-aquifer/ Accessed December 2016.

[222] nytimes.com/2015/04/06/science/beneath-california-crops-groundwater-crisis-grows.html?_r=0 Accessed December 2016.

[223] pubs.usgs.gov/circ/circ1182/pdf/06SanJoaquinValley.pdf Accessed February 2017.

[224] latimes.com/local/california/la-me-groundwater-20150318-story.html Accessed December 2016.

[225] sacbee.com/news/nation-world/article2594903.html Accessed December 2016.

[226] huffingtonpost.com/entry/federal-policies-san-joaquin-valley-floor-sinking_us_56997599e4b0b4eb759e7fdd Accessed December 2016.

[227] revealnews.org/article/9-sobering-facts-about-californias-groundwater-problem/ Accessed December 2016.

[228] academic.evergreen.edu/g/grossmaz/wormka/ Accessed December 2016.

[229] blogs.ei.columbia.edu/2015/08/03/the-growing-groundwater-crisis/ Accessed December 2016.

[230] huffingtonpost.com/entry/federal-policies-san-joaquin-valley-floor-sinking_us_56997599e4b0b4eb759e7fdd Accessed December 2016.

[231] huffingtonpost.com/glen-martin/californias-selenium-time_b_1606690.html Accessed January 2017.

[232] ncbi.nlm.nih.gov/pubmed/15261722 Accessed December 2016.

[233] ncbi.nlm.nih.gov/pubmed/3685947 Accessed December 2016.

[234] who.int/water_sanitation_health/dwq/chemicals/selenium.pdf Accessed December 2016.

[235] fs.usda.gov/treesearch-beta/pubs/722 Accessed December 2016.

[236] treehugger.com/corporate-responsibility/as-countries-over-pump-aquifers-falling-water-tables-mean-falling-harvests.html Accessed December 2016.

[237] chinawaterrisk.org/resources/analysis-reviews/groundwater-under-pressure/ Accessed December 2016.

[238] ncbi.nlm.nih.gov/pmc/articles/PMC4308074/ Accessed December 2016.

[239] chinadialogue.net/article/show/single/en/4814-The-shrinking-depths-below Accessed December 2016.

[240] nature.com/news/2010/100713/full/466308a.html Accessed December 2016.

[241] economist.com/news/china/21587813-northern-china-running-out-water-governments-remedies-are-potentially-disastrous-all Accessed December 2016.

[242] Oppenlander, Richard. Food Choice and Sustainability. Copyright 2013. Publish Green, Minneapolis, MN.

[243] progressivedairy.com/topics/management/how-much-does-the-farmer-get-when-a-consumer-buys-milk Accessed December 2016.

[244] statista.com/statistics/194935/quantity-of-milk-produced-per-cow-in-the-us-since-1999/ Accessed December 2016.

[245] statista.com/statistics/194962/top-10-us-states-by-number-of-milk-cows/ Accessed December 2016.

[246] truthordrought.com/single-post/2016/10/13/Guess-Who-Dumped-13200-Olympic-Pools-Worth-of-California-Water Accessed December 2016.

[247] mayoclinic.org/healthy-lifestyle/nutrition-and-healthy-eating/in-depth/water/art-20044256 Accessed January 2016.

[248] ciwf.org.uk/media/3640540/ciwf_strategic_plan_20132017.pdf Accessed December 2016.

[249] economist.com/blogs/dailychart/2011/07/global-livestock-counts Accessed December 2016.

[250] extension.unh.edu/resources/files/Resource000005_Rep4.pdf Accessed December 2016.

[251] Oppenlander, Richard. Food Choice and Sustainability. Copyright 2013. Publish Green, Minneapolis, MN.

[252] time.com/3752643/un-water-shortage-2030/ Accessed December 2016.

[253] weather.com/science/environment/news/water-shortage-united-nations-report Accessed December 2016.

[254] unwater.org/water-cooperation-2013/water-cooperation/facts-and-figures/en/ Accessed December 2016.

[255] cdc.gov/healthywater/global/wash_statistics.html Accessed December 2016.

[256] thinkprogress.org/climate-forecast-70-of-u-s-counties-could-face-some-risk-of-water-shortages-by-2050-a1d255ab73b7 Accessed December 2016.

[257] nrdc.org/sites/default/files/WaterRisk.pdf Accessed December 2016.

[258] consumerreports.org/cro/2012/06/antibiotics-are-widely-used-by-u-s-meat-industry/index.htm

[259] cnn.com/2013/12/11/health/fda-antibiotics-farms/

[260] motherjones.com/tom-philpott/2013/02/meat-industry-still-gorging-antibiotics

[261] IBID

[262] jama.jamanetwork.com/article.aspx?articleid=209197

[263] Gurian-Sherman, Doug. CAFOs Uncovered, The Untold Costs of Confined Animal Feeding Operations. Union of Concerned Scientists. UCS Publications, Two Brattle Square, Cambridge, MA 02238-9105 ucsusa.org/assets/documents/food_and_agriculture/cafos-uncovered-executive-summary.pdf

[264] consumerreports.org/cro/2012/06/antibiotics-are-widely-used-by-u-s-meat-industry/index.htm

[265] jonbarron.org/article/mrsa-building-momentum

[266] ehp.niehs.nih.gov/122-a160/

[267] consumerreports.org/cro/news/2009/11/report-bacteria-in-chicken-too-high/index.htm

[268] wwwnc.cdc.gov/eid/article/17/6/pdfs/10-1905.pdf

[269] goodmenproject.com/featured-content/cc-the-suffering-of-our-privilege/?fb_action_ids=10151877522926860&fb_action_types=og.likes&fb_source=aggregation&fb_aggregation_id=288381481237582

[270] upaya.org/about/roshi/

[271] upaya.org/

[272] vegan-nutritionista.com/vegan-FAQs.html

[273]
openlibrary.org/books/OL16311868M/The_global_benefits_of_eating_less_meat

[274] onegreenplanet.org/animalsandnature/facts-on-animal-farming-and-the-environment/

[275] iopscience.iop.org/article/10.1088/1748-9326/8/3/034015/meta;jsessionid=594AD9413A11E8BB5112A2C D95644BB2.c5.iopscience.cld.iop.org

[276] dailykos.com/story/2013/09/30/1240661/-Feed-an-extra-4-billion-Grow-crops-for-humans-not-animals

[277] onegreenplanet.org/animalsandnature/eat-for-the-planet-meat-and-the-environment/

[278] features.peta2.com/making-the-connection/world-hunger.aspx

[279] worldpeacediet.com/2017/05/intuition-and-the-sacred-feminine/

[280] Batchelor, Stephen. Guide to the Bodhisattva's Way of Life. Chapter 5, Stanzas 23 and 24.

[281] en.wikipedia.org/wiki/Feed_conversion_ratio

[282] foodrevolution.org/blog/the-truth-about-grassfed-beef/

[283] nytimes.com/2008/01/27/weekinreview/27bittman.html?pagewanted=all&_r=1&

[285] globalagriculture.org/report-topics/meat.html

[286] globalagriculture.org/report-topics/meat-and-animal-feed.html

[287] page 174, food choice and sustainability, Dr. Richard Oppenlander. Food Choice and Sustainability. Langdon Street Press. 322 First Avenue N, 5th floor. Minneapolis, MN 55401. 612-455-2293. www.langdonstreetpres.com. ISBN-13: 978-1-62652-435-4

[288] forksoverknives.com/the-myth-of-complementary-protein/

[289] pbs.org/wgbh/pages/frontline/shows/meat/interviews/pollan.html

[290] npr.org/sections/thesalt/2015/05/05/402584436/tales-of-pig-intelligence-factory-farming-and-humane-bacon Accessed June 2017.

[291] escholarship.org/uc/item/8sx4s79c#page-1 Accessed June 2017.

[292] animalequality.net/food Accessed June 2017.

[293] psychologytoday.com/blog/animal-emotions/201506/pigs-are-intelligent-emotional-and-cognitively-complex Accessed June 2017.

[294] awfw.org/factory-farms/ Accessed June 2017.

[295] humanesociety.org/news/resources/research/stats_slaughter_totals.html Accessed June 2017.

[296] huffingtonpost.com/entry/undercover-slaughterhouse-video-pigs_us_5643995be4b08cda348724c3 Accessed June 2017.

[297] peta.org/issues/animals-used-for-food/factory-farming/pigs/pig-transport-slaughter/ Accessed June 2017.

[298] humanesociety.org/news/magazines/2014/05-06/who-you-calling-birdbrain-chicken-intelligence.html Accessed June 2017.

[299] springer.com/gp/about-springer/media/research-news/all-english-research-news/think-chicken---think-intelligent--caring-and-complex--/11952522 Accessed June 2017.

[300] freefromharm.org/chicken-behavior-an-overview-of-recent-science/ Accessed June 2017.

[301] peta.org/blog/unwanted-males-killed-birth/ Accessed June 2017.

[302] upc-online.org/chickens/chickensbro.html Accessed June 2017.

[303] freefromharm.org/eggfacts/ Accessed June 2017.

[304] thehappychickencoop.com/a-history-of-chickens/ Accessed June 2017.

[305] http://www.chicagotribune.com/business/ct-egglands-best-organic-herbruck-farm-20170713-story.html Accessed July 2017.

[306] upc-online.org/chickens/chickensbro.html Accessed June 2017.

[307] extension.psu.edu/animals/poultry/topics/general-educational-material/the-chicken/modern-meat-chicken-industry Accessed June 2017.

[308] nationalchickencouncil.org/industry-issues/animal-welfare-for-broiler-chickens/ Accessed June 2017.

[309] thelifeofafarmerswife.blogspot.com/2010/05/anatomy-of-chicken-house.html Accessed June 2017.

[310] roysfarm.com/poultry-farming/ Accessed June 2017.

[311] businessinsider.com/the-truth-about-humanely-raised-chicken-2014-12 Accessed June 2017.

[312] upc-online.org/broiler/9230842day.html Accessed June 2017.

[313] huffingtonpost.com/entry/chickens-slaughtered-conscious_us_580e3d35e4b000d0b157bf98 Accessed June 2017.

[314] humanesociety.org/issues/slaughter Accessed June 2017.

[315] humanesociety.org/news/resources/research/stats_slaughter_totals.html Accessed June 2017.

[316] archive.farmusa.org/YBLTbrochure.pdf Accessed June 2017.

[317] freefromharm.org/animalagriculture/chicken-facts-industry-doesnt-want-know/ Accessed June 2017.

[318] peta.org/issues/animals-used-for-food/factory-farming/chickens/chicken-industry/ Accessed June 2017.

[319] peta.org/issues/animals-used-for-food/factory-farming/chickens/ Accessed June 2017.

[320] isfoundation.com/campaign/factory-farming-america-part-5-life-dairy-cow Accessed June 2017.

[321] mspca.org/animal_protection/farm-animal-welfare-cows/ Accessed June 2017.

[322] animalsaustralia.org/factsheets/dairy_cows.php Accessed June 2017.

[323] freefromharm.org/dairyfacts/ Accessed June 2017.

[324] wired.com/2014/06/the-emotional-lives-of-dairy-cows/ Accessed June 2017.

[325] voiceless.org.au/our-approach/research-and-publications/the-life-of-the-dairy-cow Accessed June 2017.

[326] peta.org/features/cows-dairy-farm-secrets/ Accessed June 2017.

[327] farmsanctuary.org/learn/factory-farming/dairy/ Accessed June 2017.

[328] cvltnation.com/the-eighteen-layers-of-chinese-hell/

[329] buddhism.about.com/od/thesixrealms/fl/The-Buddhist-Hell-Realms.htm

[330] en.wikipedia.org/wiki/Naraka_(Buddhism)

[331] Rinpoche, Pabongka. The Suffering of the Lower Realms. Page 322. Lberation in the Palm of Your Hand. 1993. Wisdom Publications, Inc. Somerville, MA 02114.

[333] Gelek Rimpoche, Odyssey to Freedom, page 104

[334] Liberation in the Palm of Your Hand page 366. A yojana is a vedic measurement from ancient India, each yojana is equal to 8 miles. en.wikipedia.org/wiki/Yojana

[335] Gelek Rimpohce, Lam Rim II, page 59

[336] Gelek Rimpoche. Page 16. Four Noble Truths. Jewel Heart Transcript.

[337] en.wikipedia.org/wiki/Naraka_(Buddhism)

[338] Pabongka Rinpoche, Liberation in the Palm of Your Hand , page 373

[339] huffingtonpost.com/entry/chickens-slaughtered-conscious_us_580e3d35e4b000d0b157bf98

[340] en.wikipedia.org/wiki/Exsanguination

[341] mirror.co.uk/news/world-news/harrowing-images-bangladeshi-leather-industry-6992474

[342] forbes.com/sites/davisbrett/2016/12/22/crocodiles-in-vietnam-skinned-alive-in-service-of-fashion/#24c28b102817

[343] news.nationalgeographic.com/2016/08/wildlife-china-fur-farming-welfare/

[344] features.peta.org/chinesefurfarms/

[345] thesun.co.uk/archives/news/193178/skinned-alive-horrific-footage-shows-the-animals-suffering-for-fashion/

[346] facebook.com/pages/Eternal-Treblinka-Charles-Patterson-author/1455353408029518

[347] greatmiddleway.wordpress.com/2015/04/09/oppression-and-happiness/

[348] greatmiddleway.wordpress.com/2013/01/10/three-purities-pigs-delight/

[349] Food of Bodhisattvas: Buddhist Teachings on the Abstaining of Meat by Shabkar, translated by the Padmakara Translation Group, © 2004 by the Padmakara Translation Group. Reprinted by arrangement with The Permissions Company, Inc., on behalf of Shambhala Publications Inc., Boston, MA. www.shambala.com

[350] Food of Bodhisattvas: Buddhist Teachings on the Abstaining of Meat by Shabkar, translated by the Padmakara Translation Group, © 2004 by the Padmakara Translation Group. Reprinted by arrangement with The Permissions Company, Inc., on behalf of Shambhala Publications Inc., Boston, MA. www.shambala.com

[351] Food of Bodhisattvas: Buddhist Teachings on the Abstaining of Meat by Shabkar, translated by the Padmakara Translation Group, © 2004 by the Padmakara Translation Group. Reprinted by arrangement with The Permissions Company, Inc., on behalf of Shambhala Publications Inc., Boston, MA. www.shambala.com

[352] youcouldsavetheworld.com/animal_cruelty3.html

[353] all-creatures.org/anex/pig.html

[354] peta.org/issues/animals-used-for-food/animals-used-food-factsheets/pigs-intelligent-animals-suffering-factory-farms-slaughterhouses/

[355] mspca.org/programs/animal-protection-legislation/animal-welfare/farm-animal-welfare/factory-farming/pigs/pigs-on-a-factory-farm.html

[356] Dalai Lama (1992). The Meaning of Life, translated and edited by Jeffrey Hopkins, Boston: Wisdom.
Dalai Lama (1992), p. 4, 42

[357] Tulku, Ringu. Daring Steps Toward Fearlessness; The Three Vehicles of Buddhism. 2005. Snow Lion. Ithaca, NY 14851

[358] Thurman, Robert. The Jewel Tree of Tibet. 2005. Page 111. Simon and Schuster.

[359] carnism.org/carnism Accessed September 2015.

[360] worldpeacediet.com/2016/08/our-herding-culture-and-what-it-really-means/

[361] Why We Love Dogs, Eat Pigs and Wear Cows (page 14)

[362] lamayeshe.com/article/chapter/exchanging-oneself-and-others

[363] Rimpoche, Gelek. Teaching Transciption. 1999. LOJONG Training of the mind in seven points by Geshe Chekawa. Jewel Heart Tibetan Learning Center. Ann Arbor, Michigan.

[364] Why We Love Dogs, Eat Pigs and Wear Cows (page 19)

[365] Food of Bodhisattvas: Buddhist Teachings on the Abstaining of Meat by Shabkar, translated by the Padmakara Translation Group, © 2004 by the Padmakara Translation Group. Reprinted by arrangement with The Permissions Company, Inc., on behalf of Shambhala Publications Inc., Boston, MA. www.shambala.com

[366] greatmiddleway.wordpress.com/2011/03/30/the-buddha-on-meat-eating/

[367] Food of Bodhisattvas: Buddhist Teachings on the Abstaining of Meat by Shabkar, translated by the Padmakara Translation Group, © 2004 by the Padmakara Translation Group. Reprinted by arrangement with The Permissions Company, Inc., on behalf of Shambhala Publications Inc., Boston, MA. www.shambala.com

[368] Batchelor, Stephen. BEING COMPLETELY HUMAN: Retreat on Secular Buddhism and Beyond. upaya.org/program/?id=1349

[369] Slate.com slate.com/blogs/future_tense/2016/03/01/february_2016_s_shocking_global_warming_temperature_record.html

[370] climate.nasa.gov/climate_resources/28/

[371] earthobservatory.nasa.gov/Features/GlobalWarming/page3.php

[372] http://plantricianproject.org/

[373] Thurman, Robert. BT65, Bob Thurman Podast #65.

Printed in Great Britain
by Amazon